TALES *of the* ARLINGTON

TALES
of the
ARLINGTON

Nanzie McLeod

THE HYNDLAND PRESS
GLASGOW

First published in 1996 by
The Hyndland Press
1 Clarence Drive
Glasgow G12

© Nanzie McLeod 1996

ISBN 0 9529527 0 X

Graphic design by
Cyan Creative/Bath No. 90

Printed in the United Kingdom by
The Cromwell Press

All rights reserved. No part of this publication may be reproduced, stored in a retrieval system, or transmitted, in any form or by any means, electronic, mechanical, photocopying, recording or otherwise, without the prior permission of the author.

Contents

The Arlington Baths

(with apologies to McGonagall)

I am a member of the Arlington Club,
And I have found it a social hub,
For swimming creates a special bond,
Amongst those who meet in its turquoise pond.
How good it is to greet a friend,
At the deep or shallow end,
Exchanging pleasantries when wet
With some of the nicest I have met.
When clothing could not be much scanter,
We indulge in cheerful banter,
And while donning breeks and vest,
Or afterwards when fully dressed,
Propound opinions, gossip, joke,
All club members are articulate folk.

In the pool, the bar or the Turkish dome,
The Arlington is my "Home from Home"

Foreword

WHAT FAR-SEEING MEN were those wealthy Victorians who, in 1870, built our beautiful Arlington Baths and what excellent taste they must have had. What an oasis of cleanliness, comfort and opportunity for healthful exercise was created in the dirty, smelly city which Glasgow must have been at that time. And if we of the opposite sex resent the fact that the club was formed with no intention of allowing women to enter its portals at any time, except perhaps in a menial capacity, we can comfort ourselves that now after only 125 years we have achieved equal rights to those delightful facilities above mentioned.

My paternal grandfather, though not one of those elite early members, must have joined the club in the nineteenth century. He probably saw it as a wise business move as well as a pleasure, a way to make business contacts as well as friends. I never saw him swim and I do not know whether he was a five or a fifty-length man, but it was in 1957, after his weekly swim, that he dropped his blue regulation pants in the wire basket for the last time. He was then ninety-six. My mother and father both joined as children in the first decade of the century. Of course they would never have met in the pool as segregation was a strict rule until as recently as the seventies. My father's brother and my mother's brother and my maternal grandmother were also members for many years.

I became a member in 1936 aged four, and the story "Gala" is auto-biographical. With a break of nine years in the sixties when I lived abroad, I have retained my membership since I was four and hope to emulate my grandfather. My four daughters have all been members, two of them still are. Now I have great pleasure in teaching my grandchildren. There are several Arlington 'dynasties' and I am proud to belong to one of them.

I love swimming. I really feel that it is a physical and emotional necessity for me. And you meet such friendly people. It seems to me that the members are much friendlier than they used to be in the days of my youth. Perhaps I have changed from a shy and very busy young woman to a sociable older woman but, forty years ago, older members always appeared to be disapproving and 'narky'. Not only strict sex segregation, but age segregation was apparent, cliques formed and the staff-members could be irritable and unhelpful. Unnecessary rules loomed large in our lives and the hours for ladies were very, very restricted. Nowadays it is more relaxed and jollier and the premises are much cleaner.

I usually swim in the morning and I find the other morning swimmers a congenial group, quick to enjoy a joke and equally quick to offer sympathy and support if it is required. It is amazing how much we all know about each other because we are all serious swimmers, though of varying ability. The interest which we have in each other enriches our morning exercise and gives meaning to the concept of a club. My own opinion is that the improved atmosphere of the club is, to a great extent, attributable to the energy, dedication and personality of Jim Brannan who has been the bathsmaster for seventeen years, years not without vicissitudes. Jim has also improved the standard of swimming in the club, particularly amongst the ladies and the children. It is a real pleasure to see him in the water with his pupils, exhorting, cajoling and teasing to get results. A beautiful swimmer himself, he inspires us all when he demonstrates a stroke. I cannot help smiling when I compare him with my memories of the forbidding Mr Sadler, the bathsmaster of my youth. I hope that I have not been too severe on that long serving gentleman in my stories. He seemed a forbidding dragon to me.

Where Jim will welcome you with your name and hand you your towels with a gallant air, Mr Sadler's stern countenance appeared to rebuke you for daring to enter his office. Sadler's method of teaching involved a type of strong fishing rod with a grubby canvas belt at the end, in which the hapless child was fastened and dangled in the water while Mr Sadler strolled glumly back and forth beside the shallow end. It struck me as the ultimate humiliation and I was so glad that I need never suffer it, as my mother taught me to swim. No, Jim's cheerfulness and bright T-shirt and cheeky shorts are a big improvement on the dour face and shiny brown pinstripe that Mr S. wore, though no doubt he had many merits. Where Mr Sadler demanded status and deference, Jim will happily roll up his sleeves and collect dirty towels or scrub down walls, even climbing high in the ceiling beams to change a light bulb. He is also an asset when prospective members come to look around as he can speak interestingly and well about the Arlington. We are lucky to have such an intelligent and energetic man for bathsmaster. I am indebted to him for the bones of the story "Starlight at the Arlington"which is based on fact.

When I recently visited the fabulous Moorish Palace in Spain called the Alhambra, I received a pleasant shock of familiarity. The Baths of the Alhambra bear a strong resemblance, in proportion and design, to our Turkish suite at the Arlington. The pierced ceiling and the triple arch, which was at one time repeated in several places in the club, were all there just as I had known them since a child. No doubt our Victorian architect had visited Granada and had been inspired by what he saw there.

In 1841 the American writer Washington Irvine after a hair-raising journey through the wilds of Spain, also discovered the Alhambra and stayed there for some months writing about the gypsy inhabitants of those exquisite watery halls. He called his collection of stories "Tales of the Alhambra" and I have followed his good example.

I should like to thank Lesley Banks, Ted Carden, Louise Hay, Isabel Neilson, Jean Reid, Jak Edwards and my daughter Kate McLeod for their practical help, and I should like to say thank you to the staff, for always being so kind and helpful, to the committee for making things run smoothly, never an easy task, and to the members who are so diverse and interesting and who have inspired these tales.

Although some characters are entirely imaginary, others are not and I hope you will enjoy recognising some of the people in these pages and that no one will be offended or regret that I have included them. I should point out that the the authorial "I" does not, of course, always refer to Nanzie McLeod.

We all know that a more scurrilous set of stories might have been written, but I have resisted the sensational, and the possibility of larger sales, and made sure that my continued membership of the Arlington Baths is not at risk.

Nanzie McLeod

Gala 1938

IT WAS VERY COLD in the back of the little green car but it was so exciting and so unusual for Helen to be going to the baths in the evening that she was just terribly happy, deliriously happy. She pulled her grey knitted skirt further over her bare knees, clenched her hands tightly in their Fair Isle gloves, shut her eyes and smiled the biggest smile that she could possibly stretch her lips into. She stopped even breathing for a few moments. She was just full of perfect delight. She was going to take part in the gala at the Arlington Baths. It was her very first gala. She had not even attended one before, and tonight she would compete in the Beginners' Handicap. That word handicap was very unfamilar to her and slightly worrying. Although she liked big words and it had been explained to her, she still did not quite understand what it meant, but, in the way of small children, she expected that it would be made clear eventually. Helen was six and many things seemed rather strange and incomprehensible to her. For instance her father, at times, called her "Tuppenny" and at others, he would call her "Penny Ha'penny". Was there a reason that she was worth more at some times than at others? Being a logical child, she often pondered that question, but somehow it never seemed quite the right time to ask her father for an explanation. She was an only child and, apart from school hours, was mainly in adult company. She often felt excluded by the complexity of adult conversation and yet smiles and remarks and eye contact were obviously directed at her. When it all became too strange and difficult for her, she would withdraw her attention until someone would exclaim,

"What a dreamy little girl Helen is! She's away in another world isn't she! What were you thinking about, dear?"

That sort of remark irritated Helen intensely and she would glower at the speaker, without realising quite how forbidding she looked.

Now she was sitting in the back of the car, which seemed to be very slow tonight, listening to her parents talking as though they had completely fogotten her presence. Had they forgotten that this was her first gala? She did like that word so much and yet she had no picture in her mind of what a gala might actually be.

In the front of the car, her parents pursued their normal assertive exchange, where endearments at the end of each sentence lent a strange ambiguity to the argumentative tone of their conversation.

It was November and bitterly cold. A thick yellow fog slowed the trams and cars to a walking pace. She shivered and could not remember when she was last warm. It seemed to have been cold and wet all her life. To cheer herself, she started to think of the Exhibition.

That year, 1938, the civic pride of Glasgow had blossomed into a wonderful international exhibition in one of the many beautiful parks. This was to be the culmination of a long history of splendid exhibitions and the whole world was invited to inspect the most modern and innovative designs in architecture and engineering, interior design, fashion and cookery. The British colonies were invited to show their abundant produce and their inhabitants to recreate authentic villages for the education and astonishment of the million people of Glasgow. Everything was marvellously planned and no money was spared, but sadly that most important ingredient of an open air exhibition, the weather, refused to cooperate. Throughout June the rain fell. Sometimes only showers, sometimes very heavily, but the dry times were few, and it was generally believed that they lasted no longer than ten minutes. July, never a dry month in Glasgow, was worse and August only a little better. It was the first and only time that Helen's bright yellow oilskin and sou'wester grew shabby before she outgrew them.

Helen had visited the Exhibition several times and unlike the adults, she thoroughly enjoyed splashing through the puddles. She thought it was all wonderful. The soaring modern buildings like something in a film. The hot doughnuts. The little sample of soup in a paper cup. The man who dived off a high platform into a very small tub of water. The little train that trundled past every so often, looking as though the people that it carried were too big and too many for its strength.

What she particularly liked was the large double bed with two pretty young ladies in it. If a ball were thrown dexterously at a target, the bed tilted sideways and the two girls tumbled out in their blue silk pyjamas. Not many people could throw the ball well enough to tilt the bed and Helen's Mother did not seem to find it as fascinating as her daughter did. They were probably only thrown out two or three times while she watched, but it made a great impression on her and she often thought about them over the next few years of her life. In fact she wondered if that might be quite a good job to have when she grew up. It did not seem difficult and the pyjamas were very smart. Teaching was another possible means of earning her living but teaching had a big drawback. One had to leave when one married and Helen expected that she would have to marry sometime.

As well as the Pyjama girls and the samples of soup, Helen remembered clearly for the rest of her life the Red Indians in their wigwams, the Laplanders with their reindeer and the sad dark faces and shining brass collars of the giraffe-necked women as they sat outside their sodden grass huts.

"Right, here we are Tuppenny, out ye jump, wee one."

"Are you excited, my jewel? Are you all ready to win?"

Helen scarcely noticed what her parents were saying as she scrambled from the car and ran up the steps to the big swing doors which were crowded with people. It was not at all as she had expected. There seemed to be no children in sight at all and there were lots of men. She had not thought that there would be men there. At that time the Arlington baths were strictly segregated and ladies and girls were admitted only on Tuesdays, Thursdays and Saturday mornings, the rest of the week being reserved for men. The only man that was ever to be seen on the days that Helen swam was Mr Sadler with his brown striped suit and unsmiling face. Now there were lots of men laughing and talking loudly, smoking cigarettes and pipes and greeting her Father with shouts of welcome.

"Hullo Bruce!"

"What a horrible night!"

"Hullo Annie!"

"Hullo Alex!"

"Is this the wee one?"

"Annie, how are you?"

"Hullo, Annie"

It was strange that there were other ladies besides her mother called Annie. Helen had not realised that two or three people might share the same name. It was confusing

"And is this wee Helen?"

"Are you all set to win, dear?"

"Are you swimming tonight, Dick?"

"Nae fear, Bruce."

"She's a wee skinnymalink that one, Bruce. You should feed her up more."

"Aye but she's fast, like a wee whuppet."

"Aye, but it's a great night isn't it, plenty folk here."

"Seems as if everyone's here all right."

"Aye, it's a good turnout."

It was not at all as Helen had imagined and she felt sick with excitement and ready to go home immediately.

The Boot hall, where one always removed outdoor shoes, was crowded with more people and everyone was actually walking around the pool with their shoes on which seemed the ultimate sacrilege to Helen, something like laughing and shouting in a church or a bank.

Helen collected her red, white and blue towelling robe and the green and white spotted bag from hook number 128 in the upstairs robe room. In the bag was her white cap and red regulation woollen costume with the large white A on the front. Helen disliked that enormous A spoiling such a nice red costume, and in later years was able to sympathise with the heroine of Hawthorne's wonderful tale of the Scarlet Letter.

Then, in spite of Helen's reluctance to leave her mother, she was taken by one of the maids to a part of the baths whch she had never seen before and which she could never identify again, to change her clothes. There she found other little girls of her own age, all in their red swimsuits laughing and chatting to each other, but Helen knew none of them and changed quickly with her back to them. Then, to her great relief, they were all returned to their parents which seemed like a miracle in that seething crowd of tall pushing grown-ups. Helen happily clutched her Mummy's hand, though even her thick towelling robe could not stop her from shivering.

"Come and see the prizes for your race, my lovely. Here they are over here."

Laid out on a large table were the various wonderful silver cups and shields glittering and reflecting the huge lamps which illuminated the pool. It was most impressive. One enormous cup stood on a shiny wooden base and there were really all sizes of cups, some quite tiny and all with two handles, which seemed unusual to Helen. As well as the silver trophies, there were leather handbags and briefcases, wallets and purses, boxes of chocolates, some with satin ribbon bows and one like a little chest of drawers with a golden tassel on each drawer instead of a handle. Helen had seen this type of chest in her Grandmother's house and knew that each drawer contained a different type of sweets. The sugared almonds, pink and white and perfumed, were her favourites. At the end of the table was something which for Helen overshadowed every other item there. It was the whitest, fluffiest, sweetest toy dog that she had ever set eyes on. It was the first prize for the Beginners' Handicap.

Helen gazed and gazed at it.

"Do you like the little dog ?"

Helen nodded.

"It is a night-dress case."

"What is that?" Helen had never come across such an article.

"Look, it has a zip fastener at the back and when you get up in the morning and get dressed, you put your nighty inside the little dog and it lies on your bed all day, then at night when you go to bed, your nighty is nice and handy."

To Helen it seemed a wonderfully unnecessary article, something that only a really rich child would have. A night-dress case like a dog seemed so unnecessary and yet so desirable. The sort of thing that would belong to a child with a frilly dressing- table and a tree at Christmas time. The sort of child that Shirley Temple often played in films, although sometimes she played a very, very poor little girl, with no parents. But whether rich or poor, Shirley always found time to sing and dance and Helen loved that. Shirley Temple was her heroine.

"Could you keep pyjamas in it too?"

Mummy smiled and said,

"Yes, of course."

This dog was the first prize for *her* race! Now Helen knew the reason for all those months of swimming practice with her Mother encouraging her to swim from one side of the pool to the other as fast as she could while Mr Sadler with his big watch and his angry face timed her. She had often wondered why she did it. Now she knew. She would win the race and have this dog, this supreme doggy night-dress case for her very own.

How lovely the pool looked. It was greenish blue and glassy smooth and the lights made little glints on the surface. The dark lines on the bottom of the pool appeared to wave gently and Helen had an overwhelming urge to throw herself in as she usually did. It seemed quite cruel to be held back from such inviting water. The noise of all the people was rather unpleasant and there seemed to be a lot of commotion at the shallow end where the stewards with their blue armbands were arguing about something, but everyone else was in a happy mood, except Mr Sadler and Helen doubted if he was ever happy.

The Beginners' Handicap was to be run in three heats with the first two in each heat competing in the final. Helen still did not understand it very clearly, but she now had a sense of purpose and a complete confidence that the dog would be hers. She saw her name in the programme with her handicap beside it. That is always a heady experience to see your name in print for the first time. Helen was delighted to see that she had one of the biggest handicaps though she was still vague as to what she would do with it.

Her race was first on the programme and she was in the first heat which she won easily, in spite of her handicap. She was certainly taken aback when she discovered what the handicap meant in practice. There she was, waiting and waiting while Mr Sadler counted so very slowly and everyone else started to swim across the pond while she was left waiting for the magic "SEVEN" which was her signal to start. By swimming harder than she had ever swum before she reached the other side just ahead of everyone else. Then they came out and, putting on their bathrobes, waited for the other heats to be swum. The waiting around was pretty horrible, although her parents made a great fuss of their clever little girl.

In later years, Helen was never convinced that any glory gained in winning a race could be worth the chilly boredom of all the hanging about.

Some heats for other races were then swum. Slightly older childen, who could tackle or almost tackle a length, were encouraged with sympathetic clucks or encouraging cheers as their little bodies in their red costumes struggled through the choppy water. Helen wondered if people had cheered when she was swimming. She had not heard them, being too intent on winning.

Helen just wished that her final race would come quickly, then she could collect her lovely dog, get dressed and go home.

At last the fat man called Bobby, who seemed so friendly with her Father, announced, through a big trumpet thing, the final of the Beginners' Handicap. He shouted out all the names of the winners of the heats and something like an electric shock travelled through Helen's body when she heard her own name called. She threw off her robe and was the first to jump into the water. Because she was smaller than any other competitor, she was put at the shallow end. She felt that the girl next to her was too close and she would have liked to get right way from all of them into deep water, but there was no choice.

Once more the seconds were slowly counted out and the others all set off across the pool, leaving Helen behind. The tension was almost unbearable until she heard "SEVEN!" and she shot off from the side with a big kick and complete confidence.

But Helen was not to win that race. The plump little girl beside her had a swimming style all of her own. It required as much splashing and as much spread of limbs as possible, just to keep her afloat, and Helen could not pass her as quickly as was necessary. Helen was second and the night-dress case was handed with ceremony to a tall thin girl with dark curls while Helen in an unsmiling daze accepted the little red leather purse which was second prize. Her Mother watched her anxiously, but Helen was too proud to weep. She even tried to open the purse, it was the kind with two little twisted metal balls, but it was too stiff for her fingers and she handed it to her Mother with a hopeless expression and went off to get dressed. As she walked away, her shoulders drooped and her face was what her Mother sometimes called her 'frog-face', when exhaustion had wiped away her prettiness. She often looked like that at the onset of illness.

When Helen returned, dried and dressed, her Mother watched her carefully.

"Are you tired, my wee pet? Are you awfully disappointed?"

Helen shook her head, but her mouth still had a downward turn at the corners.

More races were raced by more powerful swimmers. The water was churned up as though it were the sea on a stormy day as heats and finals and the team races with the Dennistoun, the Western and the Arlington clubs all gave a good reason for shouting and cheering. None of it impressed Helen very much.

A break for sandwiches, tea and buns in the middle of the evening meant that all the adults that knew her parents came and spoke to her. Their congratulations on coming second sounded hollow in her ears. She wished that everyone would stop talking to her, it was embarrassing. She wished that she could go home.

"What did you win, dear? Oh, isn't that a sweet little purse. Let me see it. Oh, it's very stiff to open, isn't it - oh, there it is though, I've managed. It will get easier as you use it, I'm sure. There you are, you are a clever little girl!"

Helen handed her purse to each enquirer with a small tight smile, always remembering to say "Thank you." when it was returned to her. She was a polite little girl although she looked rather sullen. She had no interest in the purse or in any of these people who seemed all to say much the same words to her. She really wanted to go home.

When the teabreak came to an end, her Mummy looked at her sideways,

"You're doing pretty well aren't you."

"What?" said Helen.

"Your purse, open it and see!"

"I can't, it's too stiff."

"Let me show you ..." and her Mummy opened the purse. It was absolutely full of sixpences and shillings and florins and half-crowns. Everyone had put a piece of silver in it. Perhaps they had all noticed Helen's valiant struggle against the splashing fat girl.

"That's quite a lot of money, isn't it." said Helen and gazed for some moments into the purse.

After the teabreak, there was something more interesting than the swimming races. Fifteen young men and women in fancy dress costumes, some of which were really splendid and outrageous, appeared. They were each going to swing on the rings travelling from one end of the pool to the other and then back again. Not only would they be judged on their costumes but on how steadily the rings were left hanging when they had finished their travelling. The junior children had already travelled on the rings set across the pool and closer together, but they had been in their swimsuits and had all left the rings flying wildly behind them. Several had fallen into the water. But the adults in their wonderful outfits were much more thrilling for Helen. There was a pirate, a chef, two clowns and beautiful old-fashioned lady with a wig and a big billowing silk skirt. It seemed as though it would be just the most difficult thing in the world for anyone to do. What if someone fell in? Helen watched every move with the same nervous tension that she had felt before her own races. She willed each one to return dry and safe to the starting point and to leave every ring absolutely motionless. When that event was over she felt terribly tired and just a little disappointed that no one had fallen in. She felt guilty about that disappointment for years afterwards.

The two clowns then gave an exhibition on the two trapezes, flying from one to another until Helen felt dizzy.

"I used to do that, too." whispered her Mummy, but Helen did not believe her.

Then it seemed as though there were more and more finals to be swum, but Helen was leaning against her Mother as though she could not stand much longer. Annie was tired and bored too, so she persuaded Bruce, with some difficulty, to take them home. Out in the hall there were still crowds of people, mostly men, standing talking. All that Helen could see was their navy and brown striped trousers and she wondered if they had watched any of the gala at all. Some of them stopped her parents and congratulated her and asked to see her purse and added more silver to it. In fact it had become a very fat and heavy purse, indeed.

That night at bed-time,Helen said

"I didn't know what a gala was at all before, but I know now. And I know what a handicap is, too."

Her Mummy smiled at her and asked

"Did you enjoy the gala?"

"Well I loved the fancy dresses but...I think it was too busy and a bit boring"

"Were you terribly disappointed at not getting the night-dress case?"

Annie wondered if she were making a mistake in mentioning this loss but decided it should be discussed. Helen looked away and did not answer, so her Mother went on,

"Because you know, you were given quite enough money by everyone...I mean we could easily buy the same sort of thing with all the money in the purse..."

Helen's little face lit up with a big smile.

"Could we?"

She had not yet realised that possession of money can lead to possession of goods. She considered for a few moments with a slight frown on her tired face, then said,

"I think a night-dress case would be a bit of a nuisance and it wouldn't be like a real toy. I'll just keep my nighty below the pillow and put all that money in my wee bank."

And throughout her life, Helen preferred to have money in the bank rather than have the clutter of unnecessary objects.

My Wonderful Pastime

I know that I am not alone
In the search for excellent muscle tone.
Some like massage in this quest
And some will jog or jump with zest.
Others lift weights or dance aerobic
But heat and sweat just make me phobic.
It has always been *my* rule
In aqua-pura, limpid, cool,
To flex my muscles, test my strength,
Swim up and down for many a length.
My skin adores the water's touch
My body needs to swim so much,
That in a previous life, I feel
I really must have been a seal —
Perhaps a mermaid? selkie? whale?
But certainly flaunting a fishy tail.

How many miles shall I swim, oh Lord?
How many kilometres?
How many? I ask, before I am called
To that blue pool of St. Peter's
In mirrored pools or grey seas rough,
I can *never* swim enough.

Side-stroke, breast-stroke, back-stroke, crawl
Butterfly, somersaults — I've done them all.
In the icy North and Irish seas, the balmy Adriatic,

I've pursued with energy my joyous life aquatic.
Torremolinos, Lanzarote, Naxos, Pittenweem
German Lakes and Scottish lochs and once an English stream
(Though I prefer the salty seas, my senses to regale)
Grange-over-Sands, Brighton Beach, Scarborough and Crail,
Durness, Wick and Ullapool, Morar and Ardtoe,
I've dipped these purple Scottish seas at both the ebb and flow,
When the Autumn colouring turned all to a dream
And the waves were gently warmed by the kindly Gulf Stream.
I have cavorted in all those waters
Proud to be one of Neptune's daughters.

How many miles shall I swim, oh Lord?
How many kilometres ?
How many ? I ask, before I am called
To that blue pool of St. Peter's
In mirrored pools or grey seas rough,
I can *never* swim enough.

Millport, Saltcoats, Prestwick, Troon,
Are best for swimming in the month of June.
In August, September it's great in the South
At Budleigh Salterton or Bournemouth.
In winter, if I have the cash
To some hot climate I might dash.
Not before May to the wine-dark Aegean
But to the Gambia or the Caribbean,
Madagascar, Florida or Tenerife,
Though finance dictates the stay be brief.
Mostly in Winter, I am fated
To use a pool that's chlorinated.
But I've learned to love it well
And disregard the strange, slight smell.
Steadily up and down I'll plough
Thinking of the here and now.
Sometimes stopping at the shallow end,

For conversation with a friend.
Quite often I achieve a mile
And leave the pool with a small smug smile.

How many miles shall I swim, oh Lord?
How many kilometres?
How many? I ask, before I am called
To that blue pool of St. Peter's.
In mirrored pools or grey seas rough,
I can *never* swim enough.

Lily Brown

HAVE YOU EVER SEEN the short square-set elderly ladies who guard the doors of every Paris apartment block? They are a formidable sisterhood and appear to share a strong family resemblance, with their dark facial hair and piercing, suspicious eyes. Lily Brown was a woman who reminded me of a typical Parisian concierge with her short dumpy figure and straight bobbed hair. Her face was too big for her height and her lips were too big for her face and she was really very ugly, so ugly that she was fascinating in her ugliness. She was a member of the old-established baths club to which I belong, and she was also masseuse to the lady members.

Because of the domestic demands on my life, my visits to the club have always necessarily been short and for one thing only, to swim. I adore swimming and have almost a superstitious feeling about my good health being dependent on a regular and demanding swim. I had known Lily by sight for many years before we started to speak. I am not sure how I first became friendly with her. It was not through having a massage for I never experienced that pleasure. Perhaps we started chatting at the poolside or perhaps I offered her a lift home one rainy night. I do not remember. When we did strike up a conversation I was immediately impressed by her charm. And though her voice issued from thick shapeless lips with more than a shadow of dark hair about them, it was a rich beautiful voice which used unusual words with confidence and originality. She really *was* an ugly little woman, her face was ugly, her figure was ugly, but as she spoke a regal graciousnous seemed to emanate from her and her deep voice uttered phrases of wisdom and wit. She often made little poetic references, she was specially fond of Keats, and she was philosophical about the ups and down of life. On only one subject was she always bitter and she returned to it on several occasions. The masseur in the Baths, who dealt with the men had taken to borrowing her foam mattress. Only when she spoke of this "borrowing" did one see the passion which might lurk below her calm exterior. Indeed the mattress in question was a sorry enough looking object when she showed it to me one night. I shuddered at the thought of lying on it and considered it should have been thrown away long ago and a new one substituted. However it was a bone of contention between these two exponents of the same art, Lily considering it belonged entirely to her while the other masseur obviously felt that it belonged to the club.

"But I bought it with my own money." Lily would lament, though how many years previously, she did not say.

To be truthful I often found myself unable to recall much of our conversation, but there is no doubt that I was repelled by her looks and fascinated by her personality. Although I am not particularly tall, I seemed to tower over Lily, which added a maternal protectiveness to the complex feelings which she generated in my bosom. She seemed a woman for whom a hum-drum life would be impossible. What drama lay in her sixty- odd years of life, I would wonder?

As I was teaching an exercise class that winter at the club, I saw Lily and drove her home every Thursday night for three months. It was only a ten-minute drive to her house but I learned quite a lot about her each Thursday. She lived with her younger sister whom she often described as "nervous" or "sensitive". Once we had arrived at her door, Lily would never stay long in the parked car to chat, although she obviously enjoyed our conversations as much as I did, but her sister "would be waiting" and "anxious for my return". Lily would always use the same words. They were not living in their own home at that time but, like many other Glasgow families, they were what was quaintly termed "decanted". They had been temporarily rehoused while necessary structural repairs were made to their own house. Lily and her sister expected to return to their own flat soon after the New Year. She once mentioned that her sister had been a lovely young woman and I hoped that the darkness of the car would hide any scepticism that my face might register. Neither of them had married but Lily often referred to close gentlemen friends. She spoke of them in that laughing confident way that a beautiful woman remembers her youthful admirers. I wondered if she had been at all attractive when young but could not imagine it. Nevertheless she did have a charm and a fascination that were intriguing.

As Christmas approached the news on Thursday nights was good. Their flat, which had been completely gutted, was nearly finished and they were advised to choose wallpaper, order their carpets and curtains and prepare themselves for "re-entry". Lily's sister, I never knew her name, was choosing everything "because she has such good taste. She does not choose the moderately priced articles, mind you! She does not hesitate to buy the best, but she has a really wonderful eye and we have some money and we might as well have everything just the way we want it, right from the beginning."

To me, who has always had to consider all expenditure long and carefully, this seemed an amazingly extravagant attitude for two elderly ladies without much apparent wordly wealth, but I admired their spirit.

By mid-December the decorating was done, the carpets were about to be laid and Lily's sister had bought "a most expensive and exquisite mirror".

As she spoke Lily accentuated each verb and adjective,

"Such a beautiful mirror, just a darling! We don't really need it, but it is lovely. And do you know? We are going to be awfully naughty and have a little *holiday* before we move back into the flat. We have spoken all year of spending Christmas and the New Year in the Highlands and although it is perhaps the wrong time, what with the expenses of the house and everything. but we are going to do it. We have booked ten days in a splendid hotel and we shall just treat ourselves."

In the darkness of the car, her face assumed a sort of beauty with the joy of her anticpation.

I do not know what I replied. For two old ladies of presumably limited means to go on holiday just as they were moving house, well, I thought it was crazy! It seemed the height of madness to me and so out of character for my wise Lily. However it was their life. I wished Lily and her sister too, of course, a very happy Christmas in their Speyside hotel and drove off.

One of my complaints about Christmas festivities is the loss of routine. I suppose I am boring, but I am a creature of habit and enjoy following the same regime each week. When Christmas floods over our lives I stop my regular swim and I miss the exercise and I miss my friends. By the first Thursday in January, however, I had thrown off my lethargy and was ploughing up and down the pool, waving and shouting "Happy New Year" to each friend as they arrived. I knew that the small squat figure was missing but thought it likely that she was still involved in the exigencies of her removal. I was looking forward to hearing about their Highland holiday and also of the beauties and conveniences of the new flat for, apart from her problems with the rubber mat, Lily was always very positive and enthusiastic . I expect that was why I enjoyed her conversation.

After my swim, I asked the bathsmaster about Lily and his face immediately became serious.

"Oh, haven't you heard? Lily and her sister were on holiday together in the North and half way through the holiday, the sister dropped down dead!"

It was so sad and sudden I could hardly comprehend it . Lily had been so devoted to the sister she had always referred to as "young" and now she was gone. And all those plans and delightful preparations for returning to their modernised flat would be turned to ashes. It was too cruel. Poor Lily must now live alone with the tasteful wallpaper and carpets and the darling mirror reminding her daily of the sister to whom she had given an almost maternal care. I found it heart-breaking and yet as an acquaintance who had exchanged no more than some minutes of conversation with her once a week, I felt I could not intrude on her grief.

The following Thursday I again asked the bathsmaster for news of Lily and was horrified to hear that five days after her sister's death, Lily had taken a stroke and was in the Royal Infirmary. I decided to visit her that afternoon.

This is where I think this sad story becomes wonderful and acquires the poetic touch which Lily herself so enjoyed.

Lily was in a small side ward where she was the only patient. White-faced and frail, she was only able to speak with difficulty. At her bedside was a handsome and beautifully dressed man in his fifties. He was holding her hand and gazing into her face with sympathy and fondness. As I entered the small room he looked up and, smiling, introduced himself with no self-consciousness, as

"Ray, an old friend".

He explained that he was travelling up to town each day from Ayrshire – I judged his journey to be at least eighty miles – to be with Lily during the visiting hours and to spend time with her lonely cat when he could not be in the hospital. He said that Lily only seemed to have brought one nightgown with her and he would like to buy another, but was unsure what to get. I said that I would be happy to go and get it right at that moment. I felt that I was not required in that small hospital room and as I left, they resumed their mutual gaze of love and trust.

I saw Lily the following day. She was wearing the new nightie that I had delivered to the Royal the previous night. She and Ray were still smiling into each other's eyes, though she could no longer speak. As I stroked her arm, she looked at me and I seemed to see a wealth of meaning in her eyes, but she had no need of my visits and I did not see her again. She died two nights later.

For months Lily and her sister had shared all the fun of planning their new life plus the unusual self-indulgence of a luxurious hotel holiday and what had happened was sad but I could not think it tragic. Lily could never have enjoyed the new flat with its memories of her sister everywhere, and if she had taken the stroke while her sister was alive, she would have worried terribly about leaving her nervous sister to manage life by herself.

And in those last few days of Lily's life, Ray, that mysterious and devoted admirer from her past, arrived to comfort her with his kindness and love and no doubt to make provision for her cat. No, I cannot think it a tragic story.

Wild Waves

AS SOON AS ELLA WALKED into the small stuffy room, she knew that she had been here before. Long ago, when she was a child, this place had been very familiar to her. How strange to have this unknown memory flood her mind. Even the smell was unchanged from the forgotten experience which had lain dormant for so long. The ceilings were low and wooden benches were built against the two longer walls. Two men were sitting on the benches removing their socks and shoes, for this was the Boot Hall. Ella even remembered what it was called. Astonishing that some little corner in her head had retained that strange name from her childhood, probably its very strangeness had guaranteed its persistence. At each end of the room there were wooden pigeonholes from ceiling to floor and, just as she remembered from the distant past, each compartment had a disreputable pair of slippers or sandals in it. A more broken-down, grubbier selection of unacceptable footwear would have been hard to imagine. There were blotched grey canvas shoes, broken at the back where the wearer had pushed his foot in carelessly, over the years. There were dusty, leather sandals, which had walked many miles before being relegated to their present lowly duties. There were shabby espadrilles displaying the frayed rope of their well-worn soles and a large variety of garish plastic slippers languished in varying degrees of decrepitude. All appeared to be unused and abandoned.

At twenty, Ella was a rather stern and introspective girl. She was not terribly pretty, she certainly did not feel pretty, but with her fragile figure and her thick fair hair she was attractive to most people who met her. Her round dark eyes were more intelligent and more observant than most eyes. Sometimes her shyness gave the impression of unfriendliness, but if someone needed help, her shyness was forgotten at once.

Stewart needed no help whatever and Ella was still puzzled by his fondness for her. He was the wealthiest boy and certainly the best looking that Ella had ever gone out with. He was also very relaxed and terribly funny. He came from an old established family in the city. A family whose name had adorned, for generations, the same school, the same university, the same clubs and even the same profession, while Ella's surname proclaimed her Polish origins. Her Grandfather had been stationed in Scotland as a very young soldier with the Free Polish Army. Later, when all the fighting was finished in Europe, he had returned to marry the pretty girl in Glasgow, whose voice was so fascinating and whose speech so unintelligible. Ella had never known her Grandfather, but she treasured some wooden toys which he had made for her own father, when he was a little boy.

Sometimes Stewart seemed terribly extravagant to Ella and sometimes a little naive in his opinions. Like Ella, he enjoyed being kind and generous and she loved his thoughtfulness and patience.

They were both caught up and carried along with the excitements and problems of the new century. So many exhibitions looking forward and back, so many celebrations and parties made life seem breathless and reckless and almost unreal.

"You must, you simply must come and visit my old swimming club some Saturday, Ella. You do swim don't you? Or don't you ?" and a worried look momentarily dimmed his bright smile.

"Of course I swim, you silly old ass."

"But do you really like swimming or are you coming just to please me?"

"I love swimming, Stewart. I don't race or anything, just plod up and down you know. But I won't drown, I promise."

She realised that she sounded a lot more sure about "loving swimming" than she felt. Somehow the reality of swimming always reminded her too much of her childhood. Unhappy, cloudy memories threatened to become clearer if she stayed too long in the water. She could not have described them because, as a teenager, she had always left the water hurriedly and never faced those blurred images, evocations of a time long ago. It would be different if she were with Stewart, she felt sure, his laughter and playful attitude to life would protect her from everything except the pleasures of the moment. Oh, she had great confidence in Stewart, but even as the thought occurred, she wondered why she should have such great faith in him. So many people had failed her as a child that she had learned to be self-sufficient, until Stewart had come along.

"Of course it is incredibly old and shabby," Stewart was saying, "You mustn't be too fussy about dusty corners and the odd beetle floating in the pool. It's not at all a Leisure Centre." It was clear from the tone of his voice that he was very pleased that it was not a Leisure Centre.

"It was built by wealthy merchants in 1870 - and it was strictly "men only" in those days. They knew what they were about. I bet those old codgers brought many a hangover here."

Ella winced at the word codger and also at the reference to hangovers. The first quarrel that she and Stewart had ever had was about his habit of referring to the large quantities of beer and whisky consumed by himself and his friends and the subsequent outsize hangovers. He seemed to see this as an amusing conversation which would entertain her. She had to explain clearly and forcefully that not only did she find it boring but also painful. Her experiences with her Father's continued alcoholism made the subject one she would rather avoid.

Stewart continued rather more loudly as he realised he was treading on dangerous ground,

"Just imagine, even when my Dad was a young man, the sexes were strictly segregated. He never saw any of the lady members unless he came to the Ladies' Gala and he couldn't have brought his girl friend along on a Saturday."

"I don't believe that for minute," laughed Ella, as he kissed her cheek.

"It's true! Men and women were never even in the building at the same time."

"Perhaps when your great-grandfather was a member, it was like that."

And although Stewart assured her several times that it was the case, Ella just smiled and shook her head, because Ella had heard several times before this how many generations of Stewart's family had been members.

"It was my great-grandfather who was the member when it was first built and there were certainly no women members then…" Stewart's voice trailed away. He was suddenly aware of insisting on the long-established roots of his family. Ella had pointed out to him before now that it was not always of general interest just how many generations of his family had studied law at Glasgow University and rowed for the University, how many generations had swum for the Arlington team. Yes, she knew he was proud of his family but it seemed to her a bit too much like boasting. Later she would wonder guiltily if she were jealous of his solid connections, while she knew so little of her own antecedents.

Her grandfather Bolak Fazalski had come to Scotland in 1940 with the Free Polish Army and, like so many of his compatriots, married a pretty Scottish girl, whose strong accent coupled with his own lack of English would always be a barrier to their communication. They had one son, Stephen. Sadly, Bolak had died in his early forties, before Ella was born. She would have loved to know him. Her father seemed a sad man who spoke with a careful clipped accent. He had walked out on Ella's Mother shortly after Ella was born. Since then Stephen had had a succession of much younger women in his life, all of whom seemed of more importance to him than his daughter did.

Ella's early memories were clearly split in two sections, the time spent with her Mother and the time with her Father.

Her Mother's small flat was in a quiet street on the top of a hill, where the wind seemed always blowing. There was a long walk from the bus stop and then many stairs to climb, which made the cosy house specially welcoming for a three-year old's tired little legs. Looking back, that house seemed warm and dark like a rabbit's burrow. It was small and over-heated and crowded compared to her Dad's house where she stayed at weekends. It was also a flat, but it was a large West End main door flat on a busy street near the Kelvingrove Art Galleries. It had high ceilings which seemed terribly far above Ella's head and enormous windows that covered a whole wall in each of the two big front rooms. Billowing white curtains and white paint everywhere made it seem vast and empty but exciting. There was very little furniture in the house, just the beds in the bedroom and wooden chairs and a table in the kitchen. There were big baskets and bowls with apples in them. There were lots of shelves everywhere to display her Dad's pottery. She liked that, it was like a big shop and there was lots of room to run and dance and turn somersaults. Ella remembered clearly the joy and pride of her first somersault. Margaret had helped and encouraged her. Margaret was her Dad's girlfriend at that time and she was very, very nice. She seemed terribly tall and she was always ready to go somewhere exciting like the park to feed the ducks or to play on the swings. If it was raining they would go to the Galleries and see the stuffed animals or the man in armour sitting on a horse in armour and then have a drink of orange and a biscuit in the cafe. Dad often seemed busy or tired so Margaret and Ella would go out by themselves and Ella always hoped that Dad would be too busy. She liked to have Margaret to herself . She was so pretty with her big smiling mouth and long blonde hair. She had sisters too, who visited the flat. Ella was never sure how many sisters there were, because they all had long blonde hair and big smiling mouths and they were all kind to the little girl. Margaret was her favourite of course. At bed-time, when Ella would think longingly of her Mummy, Margaret would tell her stories. Margaret made them all up in her head and they were so fascinating and adventurous that Ella had remembered them and developed them in her own head for many months after Margaret was no longer a part of her life.

"Come along, stop dreaming, darling! I'm dying to show you this old wreck of a place. Ready? At last ?"

Ella was sitting on the wooden bench having unlaced and removed her boots as directed. As she pulled off her socks, her mind was filled suddenly with thoughts of those two homes of her early childhood. How strange to visualize them so clearly at this particular moment. She had not thought of them for years. Perhaps it was an unconscious answer to Stewart's reference to his own childhood.

"I was dreaming, you know, really thoughts of long ago. Isn't that strange?"

"No, no I don't think so. I think this place is …" he searched for the right word, "conducive to dreaming and meditating. That's what I have always enjoyed and why I've never minded coming here alone. I'm not surprised a bit. That's why it is so therapeutic, but come on now. Are you fit?"

It was still early and the large pool was empty.

Another shock of recognition surged through Ella at sight of the glassy green pool with the sharp reflections of the roof lights wavering on its surface. That scene had always been in her mind's eye but she could never tell whether it was a real place or only a dream. This place too was connected with Margaret. She had walked into this place before. Long ago Margaret with the blonde hair and the kind smile had brought her here. There were the two trapezes just like a circus and there, hanging on long ropes were the rings, rings which she had remembered so vaguely that she was sure that she had imagined them. Margaret used to swing from one ring to the next, right from the shallow end up to the deep end and then all the way back again. She could remember it all clearly now. How clever Ella had thought her, clever and kind, strong and graceful. And yet she had been a part of Ella's life for such a short time.

"Are you dreaming again, my fantastic woman? Hurry up! I want to show you the showers and I want to see if you are a secret champion swimmer. I suspect you are, you know, you are good at everything else. You go into that room to change and hurry up!"

Ella smiled and obeyed. It was certainly very pleasant to be so much appreciated by someone whom she admired and respected. It was even pleasant to be bossed around. It seemed as though a really happy time in her life had arrived at last.

They giggled as they shared the vast enshrouding shower and she duly admired the ancient marble panels between each shower stall and laughed as he reminisced. He told of a crowd of boys slapping the panels like vast sounding boards and singing the Volga Boat Song at the top of their voices, until the bathsmaster appeared and threatened them all with a fortnight's suspension.

Then, leaving the companionable steamy intimacy of the shower, they returned to the cooler pool hall, where Stewart dived rather splendidly in at the deep end and Ella stepped down the four steps at the shallow end. It was uncanny, but she could remember clearly when those steps had seemed impossibly difficult and dangerous for her short legs. She shook herself and determined to live in the present. It was too ridiculous that she should be finding memories in this building which seemed so much a part of Stewart's past. She felt that she was stealing something which should belong to him alone and she could not treat him like this. It was unfair.

Ella started to swim. It was a long time since she had swum and it was very pleasant. She was a steady swimmer rather than a brilliant one. While Stewart, showing off as young men do, churned up the pool with his back and front crawl and his impressive butterfly stroke, Ella swam a measured breast stroke, alternating it occasionally with a side stroke. They were too ill-matched in the water to swim together and Ella was content to rediscover the pleasure of using her muscles without the demands of gravity. Somehow the threatening misty memories of her youth, that she always feared, did not appear and she was able to concentrate on the sensuous delight of gliding through the water. As she swam, other members of the club started to arrive for their Saturday swim and Ella examined them with interest. There were families with young children, even some quite young babies. Then a few middle-aged couples and some older folk. One was really old, eighty at least. How wonderful to come swimming when you were as old as that, thought Ella. For the first time she allowed herself to be impressed by the Arlington Baths.

"Well, I've done my forty lengths and I'm ready to go out now. Are you coming?" Stewart stood above her at the edge of the pool, dripping like a large friendly dog. She almost expected him to shake himself.

"Forty lengths! That seems an immense distance and you've been so quick. You've only been in twenty minutes. I bet I haven't swum fourteen lengths yet, but I haven't been counting. How far is forty lengths?"

"Oh well," he was obviously pleased at her surprise and admiration, "about half a mile or so, I expect. Are you coming out, then?"

It was more of an order than a question.

"No, I don't think I'll come out just yet. I am just loving it, Stewart. Much more than I thought I would. Perhaps I'll do forty lengths too, slow ones."

It was not the response he had expected and for a moment he seemed perplexed and gazed at her with his handsome mouth slightly open.

"Oh well, I'll dress and go up to the gym then," he said, "see you later. Don't overdo it, you know."

"I'll swim for another half hour.," she shouted after him, but he did not turn round.

As she swam, she noticed three women arrive. They bore a strong family resemblance to one another. The youngest was a pretty girl in her teens, the tallest of the group was in her late thirties and very elegant. The oldest whom Ella presumed was the grandmother was small and plump and very brown and had just made some remark at which the other two were laughing. They looked very happy together as they collected their towels and exchanged greetings with the pool attendant and some of the swimmers in the water. They seemed very much at home. More relaxed than Stewart did, she thought objectively. But of course Stewart would be self-conscious with her being there today. She must try not to be judgmental. That criticism had been levelled at her by a previous boy friend, after she had rejected him.

Nineteen, twenty, twenty-one. She had started to count her lengths and intended to match Stewart's forty. It was good fun and half a mile seemed an impressive amount and she did not feel a bit tired. Suddenly the scene around her started to fade and she had a vivid picture in her mind of a beach. Her father was there and so was Margaret. She was holding their hands tightly because the wind was blowing terribly strongly, so strongly that she felt she might be blown away. It was a very dark day with an overcast sky, but it did not feel cold. It was a strange mixture, daytime and yet dark, wild wind and yet warm. She could imagine it all perfectly. It was such an overwhelming experience that she swam to the edge of the pool and held the hand-rail, as her inner eye pictured it so very clearly. The beach shelved steeply so that they were looking down on the sea, which was really rough. Enormous waves beat against the shoreline, quite close to their feet. It was scary for a little girl and yet she felt safe with her Dad and Margaret. Dad had been very nice that day, nice to her and nice to Margaret. The grown up part of Ella's mind supposed that he had not been drinking that day. Then the picture started to fade and only a few thoughts were left, something about a little tree and a pink birthday cake. Then everything faded completely and she blinked her eyes as she let go of the cold rail and started to swim towards the deep end again. What a strange memory, for she was sure that this was a real memory and not just her imagination.

Twenty-seven, twenty-eight. A pretty little white cat slowly materialised in her mind's eye. The scene was not so overpowering this time. The cat was sitting outside on the window-sill, looking in at her from the darkness. Behind it, through the leaves of a large tree, the bright headlights of passing traffic sweeping around a corner made a dramatic background.

Ella stopped again and stood in the water. She felt quite breathless and yet... powerful!

These were the memories which she had always suppressed as a schoolgirl. Sad memories. Sad because Margaret went away and the little cat went away and her dad disappeared for a time. Her Mother was all that was left and then she too went away, for ever.

Ella plunged forward, burying her head in the water to hide her tears. Embarrassment and pride helped her to regain her self-control. Soon her sadness turned to astonishment at finding the key to those long lost thoughts, here in the Arlington. She could never tell Stewart how strongly it had affected her. She had a suspicion that he might not appreciate her appropriation of the Arlington Baths as a catalyst for her emotional past as he had made it so clear that the club belonged to his past and to all the generations before him.

Thirty-seven, thirty-eight.

As she swam to the deep end, she saw that the pretty teenage girl was cavorting in the water, laughing as she turned somersaults and whirled around sideways. Her grandmother, as Ella supposed the older woman to be, was looking at her fondly. The grandmother was obviously as much at home in the water as the girl. With her broad brown swimmer's shoulders, her sleek wet hair and her still excellent teeth, she looked twenty years younger than she had in her outdoor clothes. Suddenly she laughed and, turning quickly, swam away. As Ella swam her thirty-ninth length, her thoughts returned with renewed clarity to that stormy beach.

Amongst those white-tipped waves which crashed against the shore, was a laughing face which bobbed and occasionally disappeared, only to reappear in a slightly different place. Sometimes the face shouted, but the words were blown away by the wind. Margaret shouted but the laughing brown face with the wet sleek hair and big white teeth shook her head and, turning quickly, swam away.

It was the same face as the grandmother at the deep end.

Surely that was impossible, but it seemed so similar.

No, it could not be.

'Your imagination has gone too far this time' she told herself as she started on the fortieth length. She was swimming more slowly now. Her muscles were tired and her mind was exhausted with the intensity of her thoughts.

She tried to analyse exactly what was a true memory and what was wishful thinking perhaps?

It was too difficult.

As she reached the shallow end, the young girl was there and smiled to her in a friendly way.

Above their heads, the girl's mother was swinging from one ring to another. After travelling the length of the pool to the deep end she had returned smoothly to the shallow end, moving always with the grace and ease of long practice. After dropping lightly off the last ring, the elegant woman whose long blonde hair was pinned up in a French knot, smiled to Ella as her daughter had done.

It was a kind and familiar smile.

Richard Takes a Swim

Richard walked through the front door of the Arlington Baths Club and immediately experienced the feelings of anticipation and inner happiness which had enfolded him each time he had entered the dim welcoming warmth of the club for the past fifty years. Though certainly not the oldest member, not by a long shot, Richard had more years of membership than anyone else that he had ever come across in the club. His mother had insisted that he join when he was still a very little boy. It was only one of the many ways in which that determined lady had shaped his life. Although some of the family seemed to think her domineering, she had been a wonderful woman and a marvellous mother. Richard was most grateful, eternally grateful to her.

As he unlaced his glittering brown leather shoes, his movements were quick and positive. "Not a moment or a movement wasted" he thought to himself as he watched his hands. A lot of the pleasure of his visit to the baths lay in the inner monologue which he conducted continuously while he was there. Each dark green woollen sock was gently shaken and tucked neatly into each shoe, then the pair were placed side by side on the little shelf underneath the bench. When a boy, he had learned not to leave shoes on the floor as the cockroaches often climbed inside and could give you an unpleasant shock. They were as big as tropical beetles in those days, but now they seemed to have disappeared from the building, except for the occasional one to be seen struggling pathetically in the pool in the morning, if Richard had come for an early swim. Funny how he could feel sympathy for them now, when he used to loathe them so much. Mother used to call all beetles disgusting. An interesting article he had read recently described what careful and loving mothers cockroaches were.

Through the door he could see the pool. How delicious it looked! How inviting! It was a pure celestial blue. The dark stripes on the bottom appeared to wriggle gently and here and there on the surface, circles were etched where drops of condensation fell from the high ceiling. He felt the usual desire to plunge in and destroy that calm perfection.

"Good Morning, Richard! You're bright and early. Going to do a mile today? Did you have a quiet New Year? Happy New Year! Happy New Year!"

The bathsmaster's manner was that of a host receiving a welcome guest into his home and while Richard appreciated the greeting he found it hard to respond. Warm social interaction was not one of the skills his Mother had helped him to acquire.

"Happy New Year to you too, Jim! Quiet? yes quite quiet, very quiet. Glad it's all over now anyway, bit depressing really."

They shook hands and the possibility of a slap on the back seemed to hover between them but did not quite materialise.

Richard marked his number in the book and accepted his towel and sheet from Jim with a smiling nod then walked away from the little office, immediately forgetting Jim and immersing himself in the familiar environment and resuming his inner discourse. He had been a member of this private club since he was two. The bright red of the slightly rickety changing boxes at the deep end of the pool was reflected in the water. Richard had seen them when they were painted blue, green and cream in turn. He had shed his clothes and worries in those boxes for half a century and could remember shouting jokes and gossip through their frail walls when a boy. He had dreamed of those cubicles and woven them into childish fantasies which he tried sometimes to recapture, without success.

After he had changed into his swimming trunks, he walked to the other end of the pool where the shower room was empty and unusually dry. Richard liked it when it was steamy and mysterious and the ceiling was just visible above his head with its several peeling layers of paint. He supposed that sometimes the ceiling was painted, else why so many different layers? But he was never aware of this happening. Perhaps it was just not interesting when it was smooth and newly painted. As a child the ceiling had reminded him of a snake shedding its skin, with the dangling shreds of paint and the patches of different colours, but because it was above his head, he eventually decided it was as though he were standing under the belly of a dinosaur in a steamy swamp. As dinosaurs were sort of lizards, he expected that they shed their skin, too. Then there was the question of the warm stream of water which descended on his head. It was a bit rude to think what that might be and Mother hated vulgarity, but you could not help your thoughts, could you?

This image of the dinosaur's belly above his head still returned regularly to him and pleased him, but he had never spoken of it to anyone.

The hot lever on the large shower kept slipping back to 'off', but at last Richard fixed it and the amazing caressing warmth enveloped him with five times more water than any modern domestic shower could supply. It was quite delicious.

"These Victorians knew what they were about," he thought, as all his muscles warmed and relaxed. He had not been aware of the tension in his body but now, with the warm water, it was all flowing away to the large drain under the window, on the other side of the room . That was a drain that he had avoided as a child for reasons which he was never prepared to analyse.

As Richard's inner voice discoursed on the probable self-indulgence and requirements of the Victorians, his spare figure showed that this was not a sin that he shared with those nineteenth-century members. He flicked down the two levers, first the 'hot' then the 'cold', then headed for the deep end of the pool. He carried himself well when he walked. Forty years ago he had appeared as a Roman senator in the school play and many comments had been made about his dignity and the grace with which he managed his toga. His Mother, only too often, had referred to his "magnificent bearing" in "that play where you wore the sheets." And it *had* affected him and he always did walk as though he were in front of an audience.

He smiled as he considered how boring his thoughts would be if uttered and, diving in, he swam under water to the other side of the pool. After the hot shower the contrast of the cool water was delightful. He always felt that he swam that first breadth really fast, too. Strangely one of the young fellows had once commented how leisurely Richard's pace was underwater, it had been meant as a compliment he was sure, but it had rather upset him. He *felt* swift and decisive as he cut through the slightly cloudy blueness.

Slowly, and contrary to his mother's teachings, he had realised, as he grew older, that what he felt about himself was much more important than what other people thought. He was absolutely sure about this, although his conscience was uneasy about such disagreement with his mother's opinions.

Richard liked to feel that his swim expressed his whole philosophy of life. Just as he tackled a job of work without too many preliminaries, he spent little time undressing or drying and dressing afterwards, although he would never miss out on a cold shower "to close the pores" as his Mother had suggested. He felt contemptuous towards other fellows when he watched them drying meticulously between their toes or rubbing powerfully smelling unguents into their skin. In the pond, he set himself a goal, perhaps fifty lengths, and hoped to reach it, but he did not feel a failure if he changed his mind and did forty lengths. He always did like to do a nice round number of lengths and would never have stopped at thirty seven for instance. He refused to clock watch and while aware of the time, did not let it affect his speed or distance. He had a little programme of strokes partly to exercise different parts of his body and partly to remember the tally of his lengths. The pattern repeated every ten lengths rather like the repeating rows of complicated lacy knitting that his Mother used to work at interminably. First length was breast stroke, second was side stroke with the right arm, third was side stroke with left arm, fourth was breast again, fifth was back stroke, that was very relaxing, and so on and on until the tenth which was always the crawl.

As a boy Richard had adored the Tarzan films. Johnny Weismuller, the Olympic swimmer, who was the original Tarzan, was his hero and role model. The young Richard would throw himself into the water with a mental picture of a fierce lion at his heels. Then when he entered secondary school and was allowed to climb the ropes in the gym, he identified even more. He only wished that there could be ropes slung over the pool, just like the lianas that Tarzan swung from so easily in his cinematic jungle.

Then, in his teens, he was bemused by the beauty of Esther Williams in her demure pink swimsuit with the little fluttering skirt. Esther Williams swimming below the water for an impossibly long time partnered by classical statues which had come to life at her touch, but were in reality young men in white grease paint. Esther Williams with her delighted smile and her strong legs, water-skiing along the Florida coastline with thirty handsome Hollywood cadets skiing in a V behind her. How wonderful to be one of those young men in attendance on such a goddess, thought Richard. Esther now grabbing a trapeze attached to a plane and, leaving her skis behind her, soaring into the air, still smiling. Next she dives into deep clear water with her toes so beautifully pointed, only to emerge miraculously on high once more with fountains playing all around her and yellow and black flags whipping in the wind behind her. What young boy could resist that sort of glamour and prowess. Richard smiled underwater as he remembered how that gloriously kitsch scene had impressed him and remained so clearly in his mind's eye. Nowadays

Esther William's films appeared regularly on television and Richard still enjoyed them thoroughly.

He had never met a girl called Esther. Perhaps if he had, his life might have been different.

Of course there had been a lot of changes in those years that he had come so regularly to this familiar building in Arlington Street. As a boy, Richard knew that there was no swimming on Tuesday or Thursday afternoons or Saturday morning either, but he had scarcely questioned why that should be. He was not much given to questioning, as Mother did not encourage it. He supposed that it was just one of the rules of the baths. It had never occurred to him that there were lady members who used the premises on those days. The segregation was so strict that he had never seen a lady in the club. Nowadays, they shared facilities equally and they were there nearly all the time. Richard was not exactly happy about this. Apart from his mother, he had always found women difficult to understand, almost as though they spoke a different language. But he found a lot of men difficult to understand too, of course. Also, it was a nuisance to find that he could not use the Turkish just when he wanted to and there seemed to be a lot of confusion with the senior dressing rooms which changed about at the weekend for some reason or other. Then the pool closed for lunch at different times on Saturday and Sunday and then there were so many children around sometimes. He supposed that he must make an effort to understand the new timetable.

And yes, the presence of women had made a difference, there was more social contact for instance but he did not find that as awkward as he had thought he might. Of course it was a little inconvenient occasionally, but really, some of the men, the older ones, were vitriolic about the females having a fair share of the facilities. Richard had become quite alarmed one night in the cooling room when four mature gentlemen were discussing the matter and working themselves into a lather of fury. With their red faces and the white knuckles of their fists pounding on their bare knees, they might have been speaking of a wholesale invasion comparable to the Nazi threat of fifty years ago. Richard feared an apoplectic tragedy and left the room hurriedly.

"How is the water today? Is it cold?" asked Harry, another regular swimmer much the same age as Richard, though not a member of such long standing. He was wearing a green jogging suit and was a handsome man though perhaps a little too well fed. He seemed to travel a lot and to know the best hotels at which to stay and the best restaurants at which to eat, in France and Spain, as well as in Scotland.

"Hope it isn't too cold."

"No, no, it's great, absolutely lovely," exclaimed Richard enthusiastically.

But then he always thinks it is lovely.

An Early Morning Swim

I LOVE SWIMMING IN THE EARLY MORNING. Some people seem to think it masochistic, but nothing could be further from the truth. I must get up early each day if I want to have the use of our car as my husband works outside the city and I drive him to the station to catch the 6.30 am train. Then I go straight to the Arlington baths, where I usually arrive at the same time as Jimmy Arrol. Jimmy is the first member of the staff in the club in the morning. He opens up the premises, starts the boiler, tests the chemical balance of the pool, clears any choked drains and deals with the many little breakdowns and crises that happen in such an ancient and historic building as the Arlington Baths. Jimmy is in his seventies but looks ten years younger. He is a deep-chested burly man with a large smooth innocent face and a ready smile. Not that he smiled so much when the early swim was first introduced. He felt that members should not be around at that time of the morning when he had his work to do. They had never been there before and as far as Jimmy was concerned, they were a nuisance. At first, 7.45 am had been suggested as the official opening time for early morning swimmers, and Jimmy had to accept that. Members and staff of a Private club must accept rules and that is not too difficult for me, as I am a solicitor. But 7.45 am was inconvenient for me, as it meant that after taking my husband to the station, I had to return home to the West End, wait for half an hour and then drive back into town to the baths. How lovely if I could start my swim earlier but no, Jimmy was adamant that no one was allowed in before the proper time.

That was the rule. On some occasions, Mr Brannan, the bathsmaster, would be there in the morning and his attitude was much more laissez-faire. Mr Brannan welcomed folk as early as they liked to appear. Jimmy disapproved strongly and might be seen in the background, with an unaccustomed scowl marring his usually happy face.

I am rather small in stature and I know that I look younger than my twenty-eight years and quite possibly I may have learned to achieve my aims through charm rather than self-assertion. As the weeks passed I started to arrive earlier and earlier, sweetening the situation with a little judicious flirting. Eventually I dared to turn up before seven, having come straight from the station, and Jimmy greeted me with a smile and a hearty "Good Morning". From that day onwards we arrived together and exchanged optimistic comments on the weather and sometimes a joke.

That early start is wonderful for me as I am able to swim a mile and then dress and dry my hair in a leisurely way and make myself presentable for office or court. I think a swim is the perfect start to the day.

I am really interested in people. My husband, Craig, teases me about it, saying that lawyers are not allowed to be interested in humanity, but only in the law. I think he is wrong. I am enthralled by the lives of others, and many of my colleagues share my fascination. Perhaps that is why we chose this profession, as we often know more of the intimate details of a client's life than even a doctor might . We learn not only the facts, but the emotions and reactions that those facts create. It is true that we do not always see the most noble side of a person. Courage and generosity do not often manifest themselves in my office. Nevertheless, I study each life-story that I glimpse and though Craig accuses me of plain curiosity I shall continue my hobby of listening to each person that I meet. It is a hobby that can be practised anywhere. Every life is unique and I know that I am a good listener with a trained memory. Perhaps I cherish that all too popular dream of one day becoming an author. And why not?

We are a friendly group in the mornings and we are creatures of habit. As I am always first in the pool and swim for an hour, I see the same faces arriving and departing at the same time each day, almost to the minute. I expect most of them are tied to office or school hours but even the retired folk and the carefree students seem to keep to a strict and regular timetable. I suppose that anyone who decides to start the day with a swim must have a degree of self-discipline.

The morning session is not a time for long conversations. Everyone is intent on at least twenty minutes of swimming and then the business of dressing, drying hair and generally making oneself presentable for the working day gives only slight opportunity for chatting. Brief moments of vivacious repartee should be the aim! A positive quality is ensured by the very shortness of the exchanges. Who could be dismal while drenched in one of the magnificent Arlington showers? And it is too difficult to embark on a long tale of misery and injustice while the listeners are leaping into their underwear. Wry comments on the weather, jokes and one-liners and short anecdotes with a sting in the tale are what the morning swimmer exchanges with his companions in the pool, shower or dressing room and I find it a valuable type of social intercourse, quite unlike any other. In spite of the apparent superficiality of our lightly clad morning acquaintance, and perhaps even more than close friends can, I think we give each other that kindness and support, however brief, which enhances life and binds humanity together.

I am sure that, like myself, the early swimmers really enjoy their plunge and no one is there "just for the exercise" or because "it is good for them".

There is a wide range of ability and style amongst us. One of the most excellent swimmers is a young woman, a social worker, who gave her services in Romania for a year. She witnessed and shared the terrible hardship and deprivation in that country and when she returned I hardly recognised her.

Now she is young and blooming once more but she says her attitude to many things has changed and she will never again take anything for granted

Another social worker, a lady on the point of retiral, gives fascinating glimpses of her family. Because of her very early marriage and then a second later marriage, her daughter and her grandaughter are of a similar age and both graduated last year. The spice of romance is still present in her own life, and she complains of the attentions of a wealthy suitor. From what she says, he is unlikely to see a successful outcome to his wooing.

There is another mature lady, large and powerful, but when in the water she acquires the grace of a seal. She teaches various private classes and writes poetry of the McGonagall ilk about her daughters and her grandchildren. She has been a member of the baths since her childhood and very much regrets some of the recent changes. She hates the brilliant lighting above and beside the pool and she mourns the loss of the diving dail and the changing boxes and various other graceful features of the original Victorian design which have been obliterated. She shudders at the variety of lettering above doorways and the thin unsatisfactory A for Arlington which adorns one end of the pool hall while the elevation of the gable at the other end has an unhappy arrangement of differently sized doors, ventilation grills and an outsize clock. She abhors the cone-shaped litter bins, dubbing them "Pure Festival of Britain horrors" and I agree that they are ugly and must be difficult to clean. In spite of the insults offered to her aesthetic sense, she swims regularly with obvious enjoyment.

Her regrets are shared by a middle-aged couple of Italian extraction. The wife always wears very pretty swimsuits which showcase her excellent figure as she swims smoothly and sedately up and down the pool. Her husband, who has recovered well from a serious heart operation last year, only swims if the pool is reasonably warm. So strong is the ancient Roman influence that his profile could be that of Julius Caesar, though I am sure his friendly relaxed manner is completely unlike that of the historic leader. He likes to sing popular songs of forty years ago in the shower. He and Jimmy, with whom I began my story are terrific friends, exchanging outrageous jokes and laughing helplessly with their arms across each other's shoulders, like two great boys. Sometimes the echo of their pleasant baritones can be heard throughout the building, blending together in some Neapolitan lovesong.

Other members are more inhibited. A very pretty girl of my own age swims hard but seems to have taken a vow of silence. She scarcely acknowledges "Good Morning" let alone strike up a conversation. She appears rude but perhaps she is preoccupied or even sad. I will give her the benefit of the doubt. Since the morning that I had to request her to help me untwist the shoulder strap of my costume she has exchanged a smile and a "Good-Morning" with me.

Another lady, retired now, is unlikely to exchange more than the briefest of remarks but she is most friendly and charming when she does speak. Without being curt, she is there to swim and not to talk. She is a busy lady who helps to organise cultural visits and is often engaged in shepherding large groups around Scotland to museums or stately homes. She has even travelled as far as Paris. She swims a mile when she can and has been known to return the same day for an evening "dook".

Her sister is different, enjoying a good "blether" as she swims up and down with you. However she finds the water too cold in the morning usually and probably enjoys the more social evening pool when chatting as you swim is common practice.

Have you heard of Clark Kent? Of course you have. He is the retiring bespectacled young man in the office of the "Daily Planet" where no one recognises who he really is. When the forces of Evil are abroad, shy Clark finds a dark corner or a telephone booth, dons his snazzy scarlet and blue outfit and realises his immense powers to become Superman and save the situation or possibly the world. We have a Clark Kent in the Arlington. He is a quiet unassuming man with a gentle

Highland accent. After removing his spectacles, his hearing aid and his conventional dark suit, less speedily than Superman perhaps, he steps briskly to the edge of the pool and with exemplary coordination flies down the rings from one end of the pool to the other and back again. He does it with ease and aplomb, then swims thirty lengths before resuming his previous disguise. It is rumoured that his meekness belies a keen mind in the economic world.

Another soft voice from the Islands belongs to a young woman with a responsible place in the world. I do admire the way she dresses. She manages to combine a smart business style with feminine charm. I often try to analyse just how she does it. She travels up and down the pool fast and consistently though she swims with a uniquely irregular stroke.

Then there is our "Yuppy" if she will forgive my using that term to describe her. A high achiever in the world of business she is, without doubt, the most fashionably dressed of all the lady members, with a succession of smart suits and coats in dashing colours, all with perfectly matched and expensive accessories. She and her husband live in a large dream house of beautiful furniture and modern domestic technology and my heart breaks for my rusty little old Ford when I see it parked in the shadow of her spanking red BMW. She is pretty and vivacious and obviously a big success in her Public Relations job. She is even smaller than I am and lives in terror of gaining a few pounds. She is an expert in Aerobics, Callanetics, Dancercise and the formidably named Toning-Tables and brings the same verve and dedication to her swimming. Her life will soon change, as we hear the happy news that she will become a mother before Christmas. I expect she will adapt easily and be just as successful and high-achieving as a parent as she was as a businesswoman.

Several young men speed up and down the pool with an impressive if slightly splashy style. One very powerful swimmer is short-sighted and having once removed his glasses is unable to recognise anyone in the water. He finds the recently painted lane marking lines so much paler than the previous ones, as to be virtually useless.

Another determined swimmer tackles the same problem with prescription lenses in his goggles.

Then there is a professional young man who worries as he swims and thinks of the marvellous conversion he has made to the attics above his flat. Sadly the Planning Department do not agree that it is marvellous and are proving awkward.

A bearded father of four works hard at his "crawl" as his eight year old daughter is already an excellent swimmer and threatens to overtake him soon. But he has mastered, somewhat to his own astonishment, a competent tumble turn which cannot fail to impress his offspring.

A disabled young man, an art teacher, is probably one of the best and fastest morning swimmers.

We have several artists, architects and art and music students to give the Arlington a flavour of culture. We like to think that this touch of Bohemia sets us apart from that other, lesser-known, *younger*, swimming club in the west end of Glasgow.

One young artist, Lesley Banks, inspired by the atmosphere of the Arlington, painted a terrific series of different aspects of the club, using members in various stages of undress. She made a satisfying and successful reputation for herself and incidentally gave back to the Arlington once more a feeling of its own identity, as well as some welcome publicity. She has also, for some inexplicable reason, painted many portraits of the long established doggerel-writing lady whom I have mentioned elsewhere and they seem to sell exceedingly well. There has even been a BBC2 progamme for schools made featuring these two Arlington members, the artist and the model.

There are several others I should like to mention if I am not boring you. There is the attractive man in his fifties, who used to look so sad, but we are glad to see his handsome face reflect a happier time in his personal life nowadays.

Then there is the man who bemoans his over-indulgence of the previous night. Fortunately a hot shower wipes out the memory of the several G and Ts and a hundred lengths restores his sense of well-being. He has assured me that six months ago he could not swim even a length but that is difficult to believe.

Another younger man, an Irish intellectual of the most esoteric kind, has also recently learned to swim a length and finds swimming most therapeutic. His shoulders are broadening to match his great knowledge and the tiny lizard tattooed on his deltoid muscle may yet become a small crocodile.

Then there is the small spare man in his late fifties with an astonishing spring and bounce in every movement. He flies from one trapeze to the other much as he must have done when a small spare teenager. In all his aeriel acrobatics his body remains in an incredible, vertical position, seemingly outwith the laws of gravity and wonderful to watch. He is kind to those less able than himself and offers advice, but his own performance is so magically weightless and other-worldly, that it must be discouraging to lesser mortals. His confidence is such that he will demonstrate on the "rings" fully clothed, without a moment's hesitation, touching the rings lightly in the passing, apparently for conventional reasons only. He seldom swims and only drops momentarily into the water in order to explode out of it again and once more take to the air. Something in his daredevil attitude makes me think that he was a small boy who was often "warned" by the bathsmaster, if not "suspended for a fortnight".

One of the outstanding characters and regular athletes of the morning sessions is the tall and slender man in his seventies. He is a wonderful example to us all. Straight and lithe, without an ounce of extra fat and with an elasticity in every movement, he makes an impressive sight as he strides around the pool, the sheet that he wears knotted around his neck billowing picturesquely behind him and his keen eyes as though fixed on the distant horizon. He reminds me of

Lawrence of Arabia and it would not surprise me to see a white charger or even a camel awaiting him in the boot hall. His morning routine comprises a one-hour workout in the gym, then he travels the rings up and down most gracefully and powerfully, then twenty lengths swum at speed. He also loves the mountains and has bagged many Munros. Sadly his wife is in very poor health and now depends completely on him, but I am sure that he tackles his domestic duties with the same style and energy that he brings to the Arlington each morning. He is just about to visit his son in Argentina for a few weeks.

I should like to tell you more about Jimmy Arrol, the old man that opens up the club each morning but I expect that you are exhausted by this catalogue of energetic people and I shall save Jimmy's story for another time.

Jimmy Arrol

THIS IS THE STORY of Jimmy Arrol, member of staff at the Arlington Baths Club, as he told it to me, although I shall put it in my own words and add some of the thoughts that occurred as he was speaking. He is a humble, self-deprecating man, often excusing himself unnecessarily and thanking me profusely for my "interest" if I enquire about his holidays or his wife's health.

Jimmy was born in 1923, oldest of three in a Glasgow family. It was the sort of family that we never seem to read about in the lurid novels which, for sixty years, have dealt so harshly with the Glasgow working class. From the time that "No Mean City" was first published a vast group of ordinary decent people have been ignored. Jimmy's father was not a drunkard, his mother was not a pathetic victim nor an extravagant slattern and the children did not turn to crime or violence.They were the sort of people that the middle classes patronisingly referred to as " the salt of the earth". They were honest, saving and hard-working people, probably regular church-goers and there must have been hundreds of families just like them. Jimmy's father worked in the steel works and was lucky enough to remain employed throughout the terrible days of poverty which were experienced by so many in the thirties. His mother painted decorative pottery in a Townhead factory and although Jimmy could remember his mother going to work in her bare feet, he was also adamant that they ate well and 'lived comfortably'.

When Jimmy was ten his maternal grandmother, who lived

in Dunfermline, suggested that she might ease the family pressures by taking Jimmy to live with her and the offer was immediately accepted. It was not an entirely disinterested offer as Isobel Shields, Jimmy's granny, was a hawker or "auld claes wumman" and she hoped that the cheerful strong little boy might be helpful to her in her business. It was the start of three delightfully happy years for the Glasgow boy, in fact for both of them.

Living just next door to the bus station in Dunfermline they travelled all over the county in the single-decker Bluebird buses, calling at the many "big hooses" in the Kingdom of Fife, collecting discarded clothing which was of fine quality and often hardly worn.

"Ma Granny was a great big enormous lady wi' silver hair. She was really fat an' everyone knew her. She took the clothes aff o' the monied people an' then she wid sell them in the miner's raws in Lochore or Lochgelly. Two, three times a month we would go tae places like Inverkeithing or Largo fur cast off clothes an' a' the big hooses too. It was everythin' from underwear tae boots we collected. We had a big sheet, like a painters sheet, tae make them into a big bundle. We had two sheets – we used one and we washed one – and Ah cairrit the bundle. Ah liked that, Ah felt grown up. It was good stuff we got too, a better class o' stuff than the ragman collected. Ours was mair like Oxfam is now. Granny wid just chairge sixpence or ninepence fur a good coat or skirt and it was a real bargain fur the miners' cos they were awfy poor. Once we stayed away overnight, we must have gone far from home. We stayed in a hostel and ma Granny and I slept in the same big feather bed. In the morning there was a great big hot-plate for everyone to warm up the food they had brought with them. Ah remember it fine, it was an adventure."

No doubt housekeepers and maids were friendly enough and pleased to see old Isobel who could tell a good yarn and make them laugh and she and her well-mannered, smiling grandson with the queer accent would be offered a cup of tea and a piece of cake. In exchange for the hardly worn clothes, Isobel would give a shilling or two or perhaps she would produce some decorated cream jugs or butter dishes from her basket, though such bright-coloured crockery would possibly soon leave the large draughty kitchen for a smaller, more humble abode. After the "refreshment", the clothes would be bundled tightly up and perhaps with an apple or a pear in his pocket, Jimmy would shoulder the ever increasing load and the two figures would set off down the long drive to catch the bus to the next estate or town, to continue their search for partly-used garments.

As Jimmy described these forays to me, I had a vivid impression of the companionship and happiness of the tall fat old woman with a heavy basket of china over her arm and the small sturdy boy marching beside her with his bundle on his shoulder, both enjoying the beautiful countryside around them and the tall tree-lined road, so different from the noisy smelly streets of the city. When they boarded their Bluebird bus, probably the driver and conductress would greet Isobel as an old friend. She must have been a well-known figure on the buses wherever she went and no doubt her grandson would enjoy the reflected glory of his 'famous' Granny.

When three or four mansions and several villas of some picturesque little town had been visited, when the crockery had been "spent" and when both figures carried more bundles than seemed possible and even the basket was filled with good strong boots and shoes, then the two of them would board the sixth or seventh bus of the day and return to Dunfermline. Jimmy was always glad that they lived so near the station because by that time he was really tired and, in spite of much cake and several apples, he was starving. The fresh air of Fife had improved Jimmy's appetite and brightened his complexion and Isobel loved to see him eat and grow out of his clothes. Isobel's own figure testified to her belief in "plenty nourishing food" and of course, when he needed it, she could always find just the right new garment of the very best quality for her "wee Jim".

After a buying day, they would usually have a fish supper or ham and eggs and beans followed by bread and jam and several cups of tea. Then they would sort the clothes and though Jimmy was tired, he would not have missed that for anything. It was like a treasure trove and Jimmy was always fascinated by some of the strange garments that came to light.

"Fancy anyone wearin' that, Granny!" he would say, holding up some many-hued checked tweed, "an' get a load o' this pullover. Is that knitted? It's goat an awfy lot o' different colours."

"Aye that's jist like whit the Prince o' Wales wears when he gans gowfin. D'ye no like it? It's a bit rory, mebbie, but Ah ken wha' wid jump at it, Polly Reekie in Methil, she's awfy fond o' bright colours. An' see this stripey jumper? She'll make a dive for that and rug it doon tae crochy a braw blanket fur a bairn or an antimacassar mebbe. She's fair daft oan crochy. Pit they things aside noo, fur Polly."

And Jimmy would place the desirable articles together ready to tempt Polly Reekie.

Fife is a county of great historical interest and very varied character. As well as the larger more sophisticated towns of Dunfermline, Cupar and St Andrews, there are the fishing communities, the agricultural villages attached to historical estates and, at that time, there were the many mining villages. These last were where Isobel would sell her wares and she was an expert on the individual character of each little village. She knew from experience who might like to buy the flashy colours and styles and who would favour the darker, more conservative clothes. By ten o'clock Jimmy and his granny would have finished their exclaiming and their organising and would go to bed.

On the next day, a "selling" day, they would once more catch an early bus, this time in the direction of the devastated and impoverished interior of Fife, where the coalfields lay and the slagheaps blighted the landsacape. There was less travelling and walking and more hanging around on a selling day while

Isobel bargained and gossiped and Jimmy found it less interesting than the buying. Still, he liked to listen and watch as his granny brought out more and more things, assuring them that the fabric was "unusually hard-wearing" as well as being so "braw tae look at" and "sic a bargain" as it "had hardly ever been oan a back!"

Though there was a fair amount of haggling, there were cups of tea and "jam pieces". The people were poor and struggling and although Isobel could never be too adamant about a price when she saw hardship, she was a business woman and looked to make a reasonable profit. As she often reminded them she would "never ever sell shoddy stuff that ye cud spit peas through."

The selling days, though shorter, seemed like tougher work to Jimmy. Though the burdens grew lighter, the lifting and laying and wrapping and unwrapping seemed endless as he followed the majestic figure from street to street and through innumerable low doorways. He missed his walk through the trees and fields but at least they were always home early. Then they always went to bed for a wee rest after a selling day. When Granny got up she went out shopping for something tasty and they would have a cooked meal that night, mince and potatoes or a bit of pork fried with apple and onions or a fresh herring in oatmeal. Isobel believed in stoking the body with good fuel for a hard working life and Jimmy thought she must be the best cook in the world. The life with his Granny was helping Jimmy to grow taller broader and rosier than his brother and sister would ever be and he loved it. He loved the freedom from school, because no one had thought to register him as a pupil. The rules regulating school attendance were not so strict in those days when earning money, however little, was a priority. As well as tramping through the wooded estates, he loved the journeys in the bus which took him past the sparkling ocean and the rich farmland and also past the mysterious "pointy wee mountains" which lowered over the mining areas. It was all so terribly different to his city life. He even enjoyed testing his strength as the clothes bundle grew larger and larger and he examined his muscles each night to see if they were growing bigger. Most of all it was great to be an only child in a house where money seemed to be plentiful in a way that it never had been in the more provident home of his parents. For Isobel, it was the very best time of her life. She adored her grandson and was willing to buy him all sorts of little treats and use him as an excuse for a twice weekly visit to the "pictures". The Kinema was just across the road and with a film full of singing and dancing and a chocolate ice cream in the interval, it was a night of comfort and luxury beyond the dreams of her girlhood days. Wonderful! She lavished all the things on Jimmy that she had not been able to afford for her own young family of thirty years ago and she was amply repaid by his hard work and dedication to her. She was over fifty now and beginning to feel a lessening of her strength each year, but this willing and obedient little boy, who laughed so heartily at all her jokes, had come to her at just the right time. He was just the image of his mother too and each day he lost more of his Glasgow pallor and became like a well-built country boy. Even his accent was changing. To Isobel it was a marvel and she felt twenty years younger.

For three and a half years the woman and the boy lived together working hard and enjoying their laughter and leisure, but when Jimmy was nearly fourteen his father sent for him to return to Glasgow, as he could now be employed at the steel mill and his wage would not only pay for his keep but help bring up the younger children. He had to go. It was the only time that Isobel saw her grandson angry. Isobel was sad, of course, but she had had a lifetime in which to get used to grief.

Jimmy worked in the steel rolling mills until 1939 when he was called up. In the RAF, he crooned with a forces' dance band and no doubt his good looks, pleasant baritone and modesty caused a few young WAAF maidens to swoon, as was the fashion in those days. After less than two years in the Air Force, he was recalled to the steel mill, as it was deemed essential work. Very soon after returning to Glasgow, he met his future wife on a "blind date" and within months they were married. Jimmy was not yet twenty. They have recently celebrated their Golden Wedding.

"As soon as Ah saw her, Ah felt she needed lookin' after. D'ye know what Ah mean? Ah'm soft-hearted y'know an' Ah jist felt she was a puir wee thing that had had a hard time. An' she had! Her mother was a widdy wumman that had a big, big family an' they were awfy puir. No like us. Ye see we always had a good wage comin' in an' Ah was makin' reasonably good money at the steelworks. Ah could take her to the pictures for ninepence. That was the dear seats. Then afterwards we would have a "special" fish supper, that was a big fish done in breadcrumbs rather than batter, ye know. Aye, ah felt ah could look after her."

As he spoke, his kind blue eyes looked into the past and he smiled with a reminiscent pleasure at his ability to give a treat to the girl who "needed looking after".

The rest of Jimmy's life has been a very happy and a very lucky one with a "marvellous wife" and four great children. Sadly one of his sons had meningitis as a child and lost his hearing but he has surmounted this handicap and has a wife and family and his own business. All his children are successful in life. His daughter is married to a director of a large engineering firm in Denmark and his other sons are professional men.

As I have said elswhere, Jimmy opens up the premises of the Arlington Baths club each morning, dealing with the antique and recalcitrant boiler and the many tasks which are necessary to the healthy maintenance of a swimming pool. I have a very clear picture in my mind of him as he gazes upwards. He might be squinting short-sightedly at the clock, as he checks the pool temperature. Other times, in the office, when he is testing the chemistry of the pool, he will hold a test tube up to the light as a scientist might do on making a great discovery. Then the long black filter from the shower room drain is also held aloft and regarded carefully before any foreign objects are removed from it.Then he will look down and, catching my eye as I swim to the shallow end of the pool, shake his head in sorrow and disbelief at the unlikely assortment of possessions which people allow to disappear down the drain.

Each day a heavy black hose pipe must be moved from one side of the pool to the other, in order to hose out the shower rooms. The rest of the staff, all younger men than Jimmy, throw one end of the hose into the pool and then, carrying the other end around, remove the hose from the water at the other side of the pool. It is a slow method but with the help of the water, does not require too much muscle power. Jimmy however, and he is the only one who does, shoulders the weighty hose and walks with firm steps around the pool. It is obviously very heavy and I worried that it was too much for him and said so. He just smiled and thanked me for my interest. Perhaps the weight of the hose seems much the same as the heavy bundle of clothes seemed to the eleven-year old boy.

Returning

I HAVE JUST RETURNED FROM CANADA. I stayed there for seven years and I am not at all sure why I did that.

Perhaps to please my husband. At any rate I returned without him.

It is my firm belief that the Canadian climate should be reserved for eagles, moose and grizzly bears and although there is magnificent scenery, you must travel a thousand miles to find it. Perhaps I exaggerate, but you will gather that I was not sorry to say good-bye to that sparsely-populated and frozen land. My dearest hope now is never to see snow or ice again. Yes, I know that snow on the mountains is glorious and that the trees and countryside are transformed to fairyland by snow and I can remember enjoying tramping through crunching white drifts in my childhood, but that is all in the past. I have undergone seven years of aversion therapy and I repeat *I never want to see snow again*.

How little inconvenience does a drizzly day in Glasgow cause, compared to ten inches of snow to be shovelled from the driveway several times a week? And when leaving the house means slipping and sliding on ice-encased snowy mounds and risking a broken limb, one positively yearns for an overcast sky and puddles underfoot. The memory of a blustering gale in Aberdeen seems almost zephyr-like when biting winds, flying straight from Arctic wastes, threaten instant frostbite. But we are assured that we learn from adversity, that every cloud has a silver lining and that good always comes out of bad and, on my return to Scotland, I realised for the first time how much I love our moderate climate. I adore it and I have sworn never to complain again about the Scottish weather.

I flew home last January and as my plane circled before landing the tears streamed down my cheeks at the sight of the green fields below. I had been staying in Ontario and there growth and greenness do not reappear until the end of April. Of course it comes suddenly. In May the crab-apple blossom in the garden next door would be exquisite, but only for three days. Then the petals would fall in a white pool around the tree, echoing the snow which had so recently disappeared.

But when I returned to my Glasgow garden, there were still one or two roses from the previous season blooming and many snowdrops were delicately uncurling. By February the bergenias had large exotic pink flowers and the fat sticky buds of the rhododendrons were promising their usual Spring-time extravagance and sturdy green spears would soon appear against the wall to herald daffodils and grape hyacinths.

It would be wrong to say that I had missed these winter plants in Canada because, like so much in my life, I had always just taken it all for granted. I had accepted each part of the unfolding year as one accepts sight and hearing. And as one misses those senses when they start to fail and as one feels irritable at their diminishing strength without quite comprehending why, I had felt loss and dullness in the long bleak North American winter without realising what it was that I missed. So this is a very excellent outcome of my Canadian sojourn. I now *consciously* enjoy and appreciate every part of the yearly cycle of nature. I appreciate other things too that I formerly took for granted.

We talk of "speaking the same language" and I am sure that has more to do with humour than with vocabulary or grammar. The people of Glasgow have their own subtle and deadpan sense of humour often flavoured with an unexpected dash of the erudite. In Glasgow, you can use irony, bathos or surreal improvisation in conversation with practically any citizen from plumber to professor, bus-driver to banker. It makes for democracy but it is not something that you can do in Canada and if you try, you will regret it exceedingly. I learned to repress my sense of fun in Canada.

I have also learned to appreciate the ease and speed with which I can reach a large variety of places in Scotland. In only an hour or two I can drive to the exquisite and overwhelming Highlands, the soft Border country or the quaint and historic fishing villages of the East coast or I can visit any one of many lovely cities, Oban, Stirling, Perth, St Andrews, Aberdeen or Edinburgh, each unique in character and architecture and overflowing with history and enticing shops.

Well, you can see how enthusiastic I am. My friends say that I have fallen in love with Scotland. My poor friends, I do not know which they find more boring, my grumbles about Canada or my gushing adoration of Scotland. They have been very good about it all, I must say.

There were a few things that I was conscious of missing throughout those seven years. Food was perhaps top of the list and though I admit that North American fruit and vegetables were of a high and delicious standard, I did miss Scottish strawberries and raspberries, which have a flavour to be found nowhere else. I also longed for fresh mussels or a Pittenweem fish supper, a crab from Crail or a crispy Johnston's roll. I have to report that bars of Highland toffee and Lee's macaroon bars and snowballs were available in my corner store! I have never partaken of these delicacies but it was rather nice to see them there, like fellow ex-patriots.

Of course I missed my friends. Terribly. I have so many friends from school and student days but letter-writing is hard when you are not happy. And yet I made some very special and kind friends in Canada. One needs friends there.

One very special want was the Arlington baths. I *longed* for its cosy familiarity. Of course in the summer I did swim in the local open-air municipal pool and a chilly one it was too, in spite of the blazing sun overhead. Rather drearily, it was called the Memorial Centre. In winter I could have gone to the

YMCA pool, but it was not inviting on the two or three occasions that I tried it. I would sometimes sit in the evening and imagine myself arriving at the front door of the Arlington, greeting friends, removing shoes, collecting my towel and swimsuit. I could see it all in my mind's eye. It would be a wintry Thursday evening with the lights glimmering softly on the pool and "the gang" there for Elizabeth's exercise class. Elizabeth, a vision in purple lycra, would lead us upstairs to the reading room where, in the nicest possible way, she would exhort us to yet greater efforts. Afterwards, a gentle swim, shower and hair-wash and the real work of the evening would begin when we gathered in the cooling room to chat and smoke, hand round the latest gossip and set the world to rights. It was fun and many a time in that little North American clapboard house, I yearned for a Thursday night with tears in my eyes.

You would be perfectly justified in asking why I have taken so long to return to the club for I have been back in Glasgow for four months now. I suppose that finding a job and re-establishing myself in a career took time. And I was certainly busy trying to eliminate the dirt and damage which seven years of renting had bequeathed to my flat. But truthfully, I think I was afraid of returning to something which I had known and loved for so long. You cannot leave a child or a sweetheart for seven years without expecting them to change and, to me, the Arlington was almost the same as a loved one. I knew that it had been refurbished and that also was an unknown quantity which I found myself unwilling to face. What about my friends at the baths, were they still all members? Perhaps I would see only strange faces. What about the bathsmaster? Would Jim Brannan still preside in his little office? Or would he have given up his struggle with an unsympathetic committee and sought pastures new? Would Anne Smith still be massaging with her "magic fingers"? Would Isa still collect the interminable supply of dirty linen and transform it to neatly stacked and folded towels and sheets, pristine, warm and fluffy? Would old Jimmy still squint up at the clock as he checked the temperature of the pool each morning? It was daunting to think that it might be all changed and I was just a bit cowardly about finding out.

I might never have returned to the club if Rachael had not phoned me and ordered me to come along the following Thursday evening.

"Of course you must come," she insisted, "Lesley Banks will be there, do you remember her? She has a little boy of four now and she has really done well. She has made quite a name for herself in the art world. The pictures of the Arlington were what first brought her success. Then she does a lot of portraits. She's painted Nanzie lots of times. Of course Nanzie and I have both become grandmothers since you went away, too. Nanzie has *three!* She will be there on Thursday and Julie, Mary and Mae do you remember them? Then that sweet girl Louise, I think she is a lawyer but I'm not sure, she looks too young. Then Pamela, who is always so smart, she was in public relations I think. She has a little boy now, too. She'll be there. You'll remember them all when you see them. Of course Maggie and Carol and I will be there. Agnes probably won't be, as she has just moved house, it's a lovely place. Do come now and don't fuss. We'll probably be in the pool by seven-thirty and we are going to that nice fish restaurant in Woodlands Road afterwards. It will do you good to get out and everyone is looking forward to seeing you again. See you at seven-thirty!"

I agreed to meet them, though not without misgiving, but at least all those old friends were still around and thriving. I felt heartened.

I arrived at the front door of the Arlington around seven o'clock just as a member, whom I did not know, was arriving. She let me in with her key card and smiled to me in a very friendly way. She helpfully directed me to the office through a door which was a window seven years ago. In the foyer a large and gaudy drinks-machine partially hid the prestigious board which lists former chairmen of the committee, but I suppose that is a temporary situation. Concealed lighting had been installed in the foyer, reminiscent of the small Canadian hotels and motels which were remodelled in the eighties and now look so dated. Canada is now so ecologically conscious that concealed lighting is definitely OUT. With my parsimonious background I never did see the point of burning a light by which one could not read a book.

It seemed odd to walk straight from the street into the office and it struck me that much more dirt must now find its way to the poolside. Formerly one only entered the office or pool-hall after removing outdoor shoes. In fact there is a gorgeous brass plaque embedded in the pool-surround which advises us of this fact. However *autres temps, autres moeurs.* I must try not to be too critical of the changes I should find.

Thank Heavens! There was Jim Brannan, unchanged except for rather more grey hairs and perhaps I noticed reading glasses on his desk. He was most welcoming, remembering my name instantly and even remembering Jack's name, though my husband was only an occasional visitor. I hope that I was properly non-committal when I told him that I had left Jack in Canada. It is always an awkward revelation to make to old friends and acquaintances and though I suppose I am still a bit emotional about the whole issue, I do not need any pity from anyone. I realise that it is as difficult for the recipient of the bad news about my marriage as it is for me to give it. I tried to keep a light touch. I knew that throughout the evening there would be several such explanations to deal with.

After collecting my sheet and towel and basking for some minutes in Jim's enthusiastic welcome I left the office and entered the pool-hall.

That was when I really did get a shock.

The first thing that struck me, in fact overwhelmed me, was the unfortunate, rather ugly, red colour that the ceiling beams were painted and the extreme brilliance of the new lighting. With their heavy colour the beams appeared to press down on top of me and although it was scarcely dusk outside, the lights in the hall were all ablaze. Gone was the soft kindly ambience that I had so often recalled in Ontario. Honestly, it was like the one and only time that I walked upon the professional stage. That was many years ago in the pretty little King's Theatre in Bath Street. I had been asked, along with some of my singing friends, to augment the chorus in an amateur production of "Carmen". I had never appreciated how powerful and blinding the stage-lights would be, I do not know how professional actors deal with it. I had a headache for days afterwards. In the main hall of the Arlington, what with the ten high wattage bulbs, each with a bright reflector, above the pool and the seven new and totally unnecessary lights on the East wall, the level of light was unpleasantly over-powering. The traditional moderate lighting had always seemed perfectly adequate and anyway the modern trend in Leisure Centres is towards the dim and romantic rather than the unrelenting glare of the limelight.

Once my eyes had adjusted to the brightness, I realised that my old changing-boxes had disappeared!

Oh, dear, how terribly sad that made me. I would feel so safe and anticipatory in my box as I checked out who was in the pool or had a word with passers-by. The seats were always so warm to sit on with the hot pipe that ran underneath.

And the diving-dail had gone too! *What vandalism*!

After all those years! What a bald and bare gable wall faced me, adorned only with an unsatisfactory piece of graphics, a thin and wiry A for Arlington floating in a thin and wiry circle. How boring it was. My immediate reaction was to plan a campaign to have the dail and the cubicles re-instated, but I am not that sort of political animal.

I could still recall that long-ago feeling of danger as I launched myself into space from the top step of the dail. I was seven or eight then, but my two nieces were little dare-devils at a much earlier age. Janet was only three and Margaret would be four when they used to scramble up the steps to the top, such enormous steps for their short legs. Then, without a moment's hestation, they would plunge into the deep water beneath them. It was astonishing and nervous older members would stand transfixed at the sight of the fearless blonde children.

I wandered up to the deep end and I could hardly believe that those well-known features were gone. All wiped away. The end of an era. How depressing it was. Only the tiny cubicle under the stairs was still there but it had been transformed into a cupboad with a big padlock and the stylish swing doors to the senior baths were gone and the entrance boarded up. It bore an air of bankruptcy or worse still, quarantine.

Tout passe, tout casse.

Then I saw my friends arriving and felt more cheerful. I hurried to meet them, waving energetically. The three ladies stood in the doorway smiling to me, three Graces, comely though mature, such excellent examples of the good looks and good health that membership of the Arlington Baths ensures.

It was great to see them and soon my dismay was lost in happy chatter.

We changed in the old Junior changing rooms, its space now awkwardly filled with rickety plastic cubicles. I pinched my finger painfully as I bolted the door and swore quietly.

"What happened to the antique hair-driers that used to be in here?" I shouted to Rachael.

"Oh, they had to go, I suppose." she replied.

"They never did work very well," I laughed "But they were quite ingenious. Very early technology. I wonder if they kept them?"

"They always looked like eyeballs to me."said Maggie.

I swore again as I struggled to unbolt the door.

"Did you hear about the carry-on with the showers upstairs?" asked Carol.

"Where on earth are there showers upstairs?" I demanded.

"In the old billiard room, the small one."

I grunted in response.

"Yes, they needed changing-space and showers up there for

folk using the gym equipment. They have masses of that hi-tech stuff now. Unfortunately they had problems with flooding at first, hadn't got proper drainage."

"Yes and then all the tiles fell off the walls, hadn't used proper mastic or something."

"I can hardly credit it."

"It's all fine now, though."

"That's good."

But another shock awaited me in the showers, that warm dripping lair of healing hot water.

A monstrous fan was sucking up all the delicious and expensive, moist, warm air and spewing it out of the window in order, it seemed, to raise the temperature of the back courts. The air in the room was terribly cold and even in May I shivered. What would it be like in January? Beside the fan a notice warned that the fan must NOT be switched off as it was on FOR A REASON. What a patronising notice and what could the reason be? After one hundred and twenty-five years of a shower room wthout a fan why had it suddenly become necessary to have one? Perhaps by making it so chilly and unpleasant, members are not tempted to indulge in the sin of a long contemplative shower, which is so wasteful of hot water. After all, a brisk two-minute drenching is probably all that is necessary and certainly all that is desirable in that icy atmosphere.

Trying to ignore the cold, I stood in one of the original circular showers and let the two hundred and eight tiny jets of hot water attack me from my neck to my thighs.

It is a unique experience, but ticklish.

Nanzie, who had just joined us, reminded us that they had removed the ventilation system from the main hall and possibly the large fan in the showers might be trying to solve problems that were the result of that loss.

But most of my disgruntlement dissolved when I dived in at the deep end and discovered that swimming up and down in the Arlington was just as enchanting as I had remembered.

I loved it. Apart from the back crawl which was a problem with those damned lights shining aggressively in my eyes, swimming in that soft caressing water was just *perfect*. It was just the right temperature for me. I felt that I could swim until the whistle blew at nine o'clock.

"Does Jim still have to get those plastic covers on the pool each night? I don't see them." I asked, "I used to help him if I were here, but it was hard work, swimming with one hand and dragging the heavy sheeting with the other. I doubt if I could do it now."

"Oh, listen to you. Of course you could." said Maggie, "You're skimming up and down there like a teenager."

"Ah, yes, very sweet of you to say that, but I know I'm not as strong as I used to be and those plastic covers took real strength. Poor Jim had to change into his swimming gear and do it himself if there wasn't a strong swimmer around to give him a hand. Ridiculous at that time of night when you think of it, isn't it? He hasn't had it easy."

"He's pleased with the way things are now."said Rachael.

"That's great. We wouldn't like to lose him."

"Oh, he's in with the bricks."

"Just as well for us!"

Then I caught sight of the conical black litter bin!

It was a *period piece,* screaming 1951 Festival of Britain! It represented all the bad design that I and my fellow students at the Art School in the early fifties were determined to stamp out, as soon as we were released on the world. And I believe we did make a difference, too.

But that litter bin was abominable, ugly in itself, giving a clear view of all its noisome contents and, I would guess, impossible to clean.

I also wondered why the clock was no longer placed at a convenient midway point of the pool. Short-sighted people like myself could only read the time when they were at the shallow end.

Lots of other "weel-kent faces" started to arrive and the bad news of my marriage was spread further afield. There was sympathy and disbelief mixed in the warm feeling of being welcomed "home".

Everyone in my special group seemed very unchanged in seven years. Lesley and Pamela had bloomed with their motherhood and the others were all fit and successful.

After two sybaritic hours at the club, eight of us had a delicious fishy meal at the restaurant around the corner from the club.

In spite of all the changes, it was so good to return to the Arlington, so good to be back with my friends.

The Turkish Suite

DEAR BEATRICE,

A simply terrible thing has happened to me, my dear, and I feel that you are the only friend in whom I can confide and I expect my sisters would just laugh at me. Perhaps not, but I *cannot* tell them. Then most of my other friends are members of the Arlington and I could not tell *them*, for it is to do with the club. It's more than just a little problem and I don't know that you can help me at all, but I must tell someone about the whole experience.

In spite of our long friendship and the best of intentions, Beatrice, I have never yet managed to persuade you to come to the Arlington as a guest. I know that you're not keen on swimming and all that, but it is a most interesting place and when you were in Glasgow sometime I should have insisted and dragged you along one evening and then, if you had been familiar with the building, it would have been simpler to have described to you what actually happened last Saturday. You will never see the place now, at least certainly not with me, as I shall never again set foot in the Arlington Baths. That may sound overly dramatic, but it is what I feel. I shall have to resign and after all these years too, and I bought two of the debenture bonds and I don't expect I shall ever see that two thousand pounds again but I don't care. What is money anyway? Oh dear, it is all too dreadful, I just loved my swimming so much and all my good friends. It is tragic and I don't know where to start telling you the story. There is really hardly any story to tell and I hope that you will forgive my incoherence... well at any rate, here goes.

Last Saturday morning I was in the Turkish room for a different reason from usual. I do not use the Turkish so very regularly but occasionally I do find it helpful when that old back pain recurs. If I lie down for forty minutes in the soothing heat, every ache is magically banished. But last Saturday I was swimming up and down in the pool when I suddenly remembered a letter that I had intended to send to Alice and if it were to reach London by Monday, I would have to write it and post it before lunchtime. The letter was not of vital importance, I suppose, but it contained instructions for a complicated journey from Orpington to a remote corner of Twickenham and as I knew the road well I thought that my directions might help Alice find her destination more easily. You know she is not keen on driving at the best of times. I thought that the Turkish room would be the likeliest place in the club to give me privacy and concentration to write the letter quickly and accurately. As soon as I remembered the letter, I left the pool and draping one of the large linen sheets around me, on top of my wet swimsuit, I fetched pen and paper from my briefcase in the locker and headed for the Turkish.

Let me describe the Turkish suite to you.

The approach is through a narrow passage whose only feature is a pretty row of blue and yellow tiles at shoulder height. The corridor is narrow and nondescript and does not prepare you at all for the actual chamber. When you push open one of the two swing doors at the end of the passage the impact is immense. A blast of dry hot air envelopes you and you have a fleeting impression of limitless space, for although the rectangular floor area is hardly larger than a tennis court, the ceiling soars above your head in a beehive shape, to a height of perhaps thirty feet at its central point. The lighting in this room is subdued and mysterious and comes from four rows of tiny richly-coloured pierced lights in the dome, as well as an engraved square window placed centrally high above your head. The small windows are graded in size and of geometrical design and are glazed in thick coloured glass of carmine, ochre yellow and ultramarine. These exotic windows represent stylised stars and echo the Islamic concept of a private firmament above your head. I think that even you would be impressed by the calm and peace of the room. It is unique.

When I was small, my mother would bring me, illegally, as no junior members are allowed in the area, to dry my hair in the heat. I thought it a wonderful place and it still exerts its spell over me or I should say it did until last Saturday, but I must not think of that until I have given you a more complete description.

In the centre of this spacious room stands a modest drinking fountain of mundane design. It is functional, but I am sure that the original Victorian one would have had more style. It stands in an octagonal depression in the floor of perhaps four feet in diameter surrounded by a small two-inch-high coping, to contain any splashing I suppose. The rest of the floor is tiled in brown, blue and black in the familiar pattern of many floors of Victorian Glasgow.

The east and west walls of this chamber are the shorter sides of this rectangular room. On either side of the east wall is a set of two swing doors, those on the left being the doors through which you have entered. The doors on the right lead to a small separate apartment, a sort of annexe. This is the only entrance to that annexe and I want you to bear this in mind, Beatrice. In the wall between the two sets of doors are three large arched windows through which the small room beyond is visible and you are able to see the interior quite clearly at a glance. The motif of three arches is, or used to be, repeated throughout the club and can also be seen at the entrance to the premises. In this small room the ceiling is only about ten feet high with a skylight which gives little light and on a typical rainy Glasgow day this inner sanctum is even dimmer and more shadowy than the main room. When I was a child it always struck me as being very like a shop window as it has much the same proportions as the area of a display window and it seemed especially similar if a partially-draped and sleeping lady was slumped on a chair like a waxwork figure. What is different about this sudsidiary room is its extreme temperature. In this little room it is very, *very* hot and as dry as the desert. Its proper name is the caldarium though no one calls it that. I can just hear you saying "Aye that sounds mair like a cauld room than a hot room." Believe me it is hot and on entering this fiery apartment, the skin inside your nose and mouth become parched in moments and even to touch the wooden furniture is painfully hot for bare flesh. I have never been able to stand the heat in there for more than a few minutes and when you emerge once more to the large domed hall it seems by contrast almost cool, where previously one would have called it very hot.

The furniture of the Turkish suite is extremely simple and utilitarian and is constructed of wooden slats. Around the walls of the large room are eight couches or divans, each with a wooden pillow. I can vouch that these are wonderfully comfortable to lie on and most therapeutic for my bad back. Above each divan is a small crystal lamp giving sufficient light to read by, without disturbing the equanimity of other more somnolent members. Beside each lamp is a bell-push to summon aid should it be required. Around the enclosed fountain are twelve excellently designed lounging chairs with gently sloping backs and extended leg-rests, reminiscent of the chairs on the deck of an ocean liner. They must be the original chairs and though comfortable are perhaps slightly large for average feminine proportions because, of course, there were no lady members in the club until well into this century. Four other modern chairs have a more obtuse angle between seat and back and are altogether less successful ergonomically. The smaller hotter room has two divans and three chairs.

Last Saturday at 11 am the Turkish suite was absolutely empty. I examined it carefully and there was not a drop of water around the drinking fountain and not a magazine or towel or sheet was lying around. No one had yet made use of its sybaritic delights. I congratulated myself on choosing this secluded corner to concentrate on my letter-writing and I chose to sit in the first chair that I came to, which meant I was facing the fountain in the centre of the room with my back to the three arched windows of the hot room. By turning my head just slightly to the right I would be able to give a friendly but stand-offish smile to anyone who entered the suite and threatened my privacy. We are not supposed to chat in that temple of relaxation, but if only one or two ladies are foregathered there, no doubt a vivacious conversation might quickly ensue and I wanted to avoid that in order to finish my letter.

I started immediately. There is no point in describing what I had to tell Alice. It was a series of directions and a list of objects. It was the sort of letter which needs no style or humour but takes concentration to make sure it is accurate. I had to imagine the streets through which she would drive, the traffic lights, the roundabouts, the salient features which would tell her whether she had strayed from her route or not, you know the type of thing. At first I wrote quickly, then had to pause several times to visualise a particular area. It was during one of these pauses, I was staring at the coloured windows high above me for inspiration, that I heard the soft quick brush of the swing doors opening, followed by the series of little diminishing brushes which happen when the door is allowed to swing free. I turned my head immediately with a friendly-but-preoccupied expression on my face, but no one was there. That often happens of course, when people realise as they are about to enter that they have left their book, spectacles, hairbrush or other necessity somewhere else in the building and must fetch them. You can imagine how the warmth and relaxation of the club are apt to aggravate any tendency to absent-mindedness.

I returned to my mental drive through the suburbs of London with a sigh of relief which echoed the sigh of the closing door.

Beatrice, here I must talk about something which you may not have noticed particularly. I do not mean that you are less observant than I am but living in the country you may not have had the opportunities that I have had to study swing doors. No really I am not going crazy, I can just hear you shouting with laughter but *honestly* swing doors and the way that they behave are important to this story. I have always liked swing doors. As a child all the important buildings in my life had swing doors. My grandmother had them in her house and there were several at the baths and all the big shops had them. I suppose I was fascinated by them. I was an *authority* on which were stiff and dangerous to a child and which were easy and charming to pass through. Each swing door, or set of swing doors as they often come in pairs, has an individual way of behaving and sounding, have you ever noticed? I made quite a study of it as a child. No wonder my sisters thought me queer! Well anyway, the entrance doors to the Turkish are easy to push open and make, as I said, a brushing sound which is repeated two or three times as the doors swing back and forth against each other until they lose their momentum. The doors to the hot room on the other hand, although they appear similar, are very heavy to push and make no further movement after they are pushed. They also make a distinct creak when opened which is repeated in a different key when they close. The difference in sound of the two sets of doors is unmistakeable. During the last thirty years I have lain on my wooden divan many times and even though my eyes were shut I could monitor the comings and goings of my fellow members with ease.

Where was I? Oh yes. Someone had come to the entrance then decided against coming in at that particular moment, a straightforward situation and I returned to the task that I had set myself. After a few moments of thought, I was about to write again when, as often happens in any part of the club, my nostrils were gently assailed by a subtle perfume. I think I must have quite a few canine genes or DNA or whatever it is in my makeup as I have a such a strong sense of smell and enjoy the sensation of all smells, even unpleasant ones. A smell reaffirms one's physical self and ability to partake of the world around us. I know that I am *alive* when I smell something and this was a very pleasant smell indeed, not at all like the sickly scent of some aftershaves or the overpowering musk of the modern perfume and it was certainly not the fresh antiseptic smell of Vim or Thomson's cleaner, that abrasive pink paste beloved of Glasgow housewives and the Arlington staff. All of those aromas are often to be sniffed around the club premises. No, this was a delicious and delicately old-fashioned floral perfume. Where could it be coming from?

I sat forward and looked around but the two rooms were still absolutely empty.

I returned to my letter and directed Alice another mile on her long journey. I had guided her practically to her destination when I became aware that the faint perfume had become much, much stronger. And I could recognise it! Without doubt, it was the scent of an old-fashioned Persian rose and one which I had in my garden. I was quite positive. It was the scent of the thornless Zephrin Drouin, which has grown for years outside my sitting-room window and, when struck by the strong evening sun, exudes an exquisite and hypnotising fragrance from its deep pink blooms. But this perfume was now intensifying in a very unpleasant way. It was so powerful, so chokingly strong that I became alarmed. It was almost more than I could stand and it was inexplicable. There was no one else in the room. Could it possibly be an escape of gas which smelled miraculously like roses? What was it? I jumped to my feet and gathered up my belongings. Should I escape before I was completely overcome? You know what myriad and foolish thoughts can fly desperately through your mind in a few seconds. As I stood there trying not to inhale and yet breathing rather heavily, the choking smell faded and disappeared. Or as far as I could judge, it disappeared. My olfactory sense had been so abused that I could believe neither in the presence nor the absence of that smell of roses.

Once the panic had passed, I felt terribly stupid and sat down again. What on earth was the matter with me? I had imagined it all of course, though it seemed as though vestiges of the fragrance still lingered in my memory.

I felt rather shaken, but I resumed my letter and as it was only eleven-thirty now and the directions were complete, I added an anecdote about my cat and her ridiculous games, she is such a quaint character. I know Alice always enjoys a giggle in my letters and this had been a very boring epistle so far. The creativity involved in depicting my zany little black cat calmed me down too. As I signed the letter the perfume once more wafted past me very faintly and the phrase "Attar of Roses" popped into my mind. As far as I know, I have never smelt Attar, or as it is sometimes known, Otto of Roses, but it is a name which has always appealed to me, conjuring up visions of scenes in the harem, with plashing fountains and flighting swallows and diaphanously veiled women recumbent on silken cushions, but then I needn't tell you what an old romantic I am. I looked up to the star-like windows above me and I suppose I was listening in my mind to the phrase Attar of Roses and seeing in my mind's eye the gardens of the Alhambra. I have never visited that traceried citadel but feel I know it well because of the postcards which I have received from adventurous friends. I expect I was smiling.

Suddenly I heard the long slow sweep and the special creak to and fro of the heavy door leading to the caldarium.

This was impossible as no one else was in the greater chamber and my stomach contracted and a coldness rushed over the skin of my shoulders and arms. I was suddenly desperately afraid, too afraid to move or look to my left. No one had entered the large chamber and therefore no one could enter the smaller one. My ballpoint pen fell from my hand and, slipping through the slats of the chair, fell to the floor with a small everyday comforting noise.

As I sat, the faint waft of perfume strengthened once again.

And now I am very unsure of what happened next. I was in such a state of terror, so petrified that I cannot answer for the truth of the next statements.

First, from the hot room, but muffled and distant, I heard a very faint exclamation, almost a scream. Next I heard a sound that, at first, had a cosy domestic familiarity but which I could not quite place. Then I realised that, although also distant, it was the same sound that rang through our house every Sunday evening when my Grandmother would sharpen her great carving knife ready to cut the roast beef.

But this was a slower, more aggressive rhythm, as though the knife were longer, sharper and *curved.* The sound lasted for several seconds and it filled me with horror.

Next a man's voice faint and muffled, but angry, shouted out. Then there was a great clattering noise which seemed almost beside me. It sounded like a very large piece of steel falling to the hard floor.

I lay back in the chair trying to control myself. I forced myself to think of the small noise which my plastic pen had made when it fell as that seemed my only contact with reality. I saw nothing at all as it seemed to be happening behind me in that small hot room and my muscles were so completely without strength that I could not have forced myself to turn my head at that moment for all the riches of the orient.

Then once more I heard the heavy door of the caldarium slowly open and shut with the two distinctive creaking notes. The scent of roses had completely disappeared and a hot pungent odour had taken its place.

It was a sickening odour, which I was afraid to name.

With an effort of will I turned my head to the right and watched the entrance door for some moments but nothing was to be seen and I closed my eyes briefly. I felt terribly weak and felt I must leave this horrible place and see another human being as quickly as possible. I thought longingly of the pool with laughing, splashing children and boys swinging on the trapeze and cheerful groups chatting round the edge, but I scarcely felt able to move from my chair. I thought of familiar faces in the boot hall or the bar and yearned to touch a hand or arm, it seemed so long since I had experienced human contact.

With difficulty I stood up, picking up my letter but allowing my pen to remain where it had fallen.

I turned and forced myself to look into the depths of the "shop window". It was almost murky, as so little light was filtering through the ground glass skylight but there was certainly no one there. One thing was different though. On first entering the suite that morning I had seen no evidence of anyone else having been there before me. I had noticed particularly as I had been so keen to have privacy to write my letter. But now, over the back of one of the chairs in the small room, lay a sheet similar to the one that I myself wore. As I peered nervously through the window I realised that it was much larger and not so white as the regulation sheet and as my eyes became more accustomed to the gloom I saw that it must be of a finer texture as it hung in tiny folds, reminiscent of the drapery of a classical Greek statue. As this realisation came to me, it seemed like another inexplicable horror and I stepped back quickly. As I moved the fabric started to slide very slowly from the chair-back and with the unreal drift of finest silk chiffon, it fluttered and wafted gracefully to the floor where it lay in a small sinister heap. As it fell, and it took an unconscionable time to fall, I had the impression of the dull glitter of gold thread but, as I said before, I cannot answer for any of my senses at that moment. While I gazed through the window, suddenly both doors to the corridor opened briskly and I looked around with relief and delight. How much I needed to see a fellow member at that moment! I felt that I had lost all the strength and will-power that I required to leave that over-heated domed chamber.

The doors were thrust out into the corridor and were opened to their maximum then, as usual, they shut and bumped against each other with their diminishing series of brushes and bumps.

From where I stood I could see that there was no one on either side of those doors.

Beatrice, I cannot remember what happened next but I must have run from the Turkish suite because I found myself sitting, helpless and trembling, in one of the deep armchairs in what is called the tepidarium or cooling room which is just along the corridor. A beautiful girl, Rita, was brushing her hair at the mirror. My good friend Barbara was sitting beside me anointing her legs with oil and bemoaning her desire for chocolate in the middle of her latest diet. Louise and Mary were discussing the navy jackets in Marks and Spencers. Oh Beatrice, it was so wonderfully normal that the tears sprang into my eyes. When Barbara noticed them, I passed it off as the result of the chlorine being especially strong in the pool that morning and my eyes do water after a swim sometimes. On the pretext of admiring her towelling robe I stroked her sleeve and felt the warm human arm beneath it. I do not know if she noticed my trembling hand, but she said nothing. What I really wanted was to grab her and hug her, but I restrained myself.

I stayed in the cooling room for an hour until I recovered my equanimity and the letter to Alice was never posted.

Beatrice, what am I to do? I have been a member of the Arlington for more years than practically anyone else. After all these years of membership, how can I explain that I am leaving? I cannot tell them that the Arlington is haunted. Who would listen to that story? I hardly believe it myself. I do not want to leave but I know that I could never use my keycard again to enter the building with the memory of that dreadful experience in the Turkish in my head, I could not do it. And what shall I say to Alice and Sarah when they return to Scotland? Shall I warn them away from the club which they have attended since they were babies and of which they are so proud to be fourth generation members? How shall I manage without my wonderful swimming that keeps me so healthy?

And without yoga on a Tuesday? And without water aerobics on a Thursday? And without my massage and without my chiropodist? And Jim was helping me so much with my back crawl, too. I was really getting somewhere. It's really awful. And my bad back! Of course *I shall never lie on one of those wooden divans again*.

And my friends! Can I allow them to risk having the same dreadful experience that I had, without warning them?

Oh dear, all those memories of my childhood and my daughters' childhood all to be wiped away, how shall I divorce myself from all those beautiful memories? And I can *never* mention the whole business to my sisters. They have always thought my obsession with the Arlington ridiculous anyway and they won't believe a word of my experience in the Turkish room.

Dearest Beatrice, please come and visit me very soon, I know it will help me to see you. I need your advice and your sane presence. Please come soon, please,

Your very good friend,

Sybil

P.S. When I returned home on Saturday, I went into the garden and somehow found enough strength to hack down my Zephrin Drouin bush. I tried to dig it out, but it has been established for more than twenty years and it was too much for me and I shall have to employ someone to remove the root. This is another loss because it was a beautiful rose, but my nostrils must never again be assailed by that perfume.

The Winner

WHEN LYDIA WAS SIXTEEEN, she won a beauty contest. Not a large international one, just one of the many small contests which were held up and down the amazingly long coastline of Britain in the days before the Feminist Movement had pointed out how very wrong-minded a thing is a beauty contest. At the annual family holiday on the Clyde, her cousins had persuaded her to enter the local contest and winning it, she became for a day Miss Skelmorlie or perhaps Miss Seamill, I forget. She was a pretty girl with a lovely figure and she was the only one who was surprised that she was the winner.

In later years, she often recalled that day of triumph with pleasure and always felt that she walked taller and more beautifully than she normally did when she thought of it.

She remembered two or three of the other contestants pushing handkerchiefs into the top of their swimsuits to accentuate their bosoms. It had seemed a bit like cheating to Lydia, but as they were all so jolly and they made no secret of what they were doing, she could not feel aggrieved. It was really good fun, she remembered, with a lot of giggling and one tall thin girl had borrowed her lipstick "just for luck".

But the beauty contest was only one triumph amongst many. Lydia was a brilliant and hard-working schoolgirl and student, an excellent tennis player, a dedicated Girl Guide, a leading soprano in the church choir and an all round 'nice girl'. Ink never stained her fingers, ladders never sullied her stockings and her gently curling brown hair seemed impervious to rain and wind. On Thursday nights, for recreation, she liked to bake a cake and some biscuits "to fill up the boxes" as her father had a very sweet tooth. She was the sort of girl whom we all think we should like as a daughter. Of course other girls, who might be fond of her as a person, did dislike to hear any reference made to her or to her attainments by their own parents and Lydia was never what is known as a popular girl.

Lydia walked around the edge of the Arlington pool from the senior changing rooms, taking the long route past the bathing boxes. She was unself-conscious, unlike other members, whose pleasure in the delights of the dinner table made it desirable that, when in all-revealing swimsuits, they should choose the shortest distance between two points. Though it was thirty years since she had worn the diagonal sash and the little tin crown at Skelmorlie, or Seamill, her figure was still faultless and her carriage superb. As she walked towards the shallow end, tucking her still dark curls into her white bathing cap, perhaps subconsciously she re-lived the resounding cheers and the chilly wind on her thighs of that long ago July day on the Clyde.

At the shallow end, deeper in conversation than in the water, were five ladies who greeted Lydia as she passed by. She smiled warmly and waved enthusiastically. As soon as she had disappeared into the showers, the group, in unison, immersed themselves to the neck to continue their discussion.

After her shower, Lydia returned to the pool and descended the steps at the shallow end gracefully. After exchanging a few words with the five heads in the water, she started to swim. Fifteen lengths of the breast stroke was her twice weekly exercise. Swimming was not one of her more successful attainments and with her head held high out of the water (to protect her hair as much as possible) her chin sticking forward and a slightly jerky stroke, Lydia lost some of her magical superiority in the water. There were those who were not sorry to note this tumble from the pedestal of perfection. Lydia was aware of her aquatic deficiencies and it says a lot for her character that she continued to swim regularly and would, on no account, have avoided her twice weekly visits to the club.

In the previous year, the Arlington club had acquired, at considerable expense, a variety of high-tech gymnastic equipment. Shiny tubular steel, glossy leather pads and calibrated lead weights were fashioned into intimidating instruments of correction for all figure faults. Some members, and not just the younger ones, welcomed these innovations with delight and started to speak knowledgeably of triceps and deltoids, upper and lower abdominals and, even more incomprehensible, pecs and quads. Other members bemoaned the good old days of the parallel bars and the Indian clubs and the quaint Victorian rowing machine. Most members, as always, stayed downstairs and enjoyed the pool, the Turkish and the bar.

Lydia, with some trepidation, had sampled the opening and shutting and the pulling and pushing required in this shiny new gym and found that she enjoyed using her muscles. With the help and advice of David, the gymnastic expert, she added an exercise progamme to her swim, on her twice-weekly visits to the club, and for five months she worked diligently and found it very satisfying to exert herself to sweating point. The gymnasium exerted a sort of fascination over her and sometimes she would forgo her swim altogether and spend an extra thirty minutes working out. She knew that she was getting much stronger and rejoiced in being so powerful. Her heavy briefcase seemed light and airy and she would hardly notice the effort required to run up several flights of stairs. As she sat in her office on Tuesdays and Thursdays she found herself thinking of each machine and how she would use it and enjoy it that evening when she went to the Arlington.

After five months she stopped her visits to gym. She could not have explained exactly why she stopped, but she did and returned to her twice-weekly swim of fifteen lengths.

As Lydia swam up and down, that distant Clydeside day of bright sun and lowering clouds came into her mind once again.

Why did winning that contest have such significance for her?

The memory and the question occurred to her frequently. Not even the accolade of receiving her PhD and strolling in her bright hooded gown through the University cloisters with the congratulations of her family and colleagues ringing in her ears, seemed to have the same impact. It was inexplicable and she pondered various explanations. Perhaps she had studied so hard that she felt no suprise at receiving a degree, her work justified it. That other time was different and though truthfully the whole business was quite tacky and embarrassing in retrospect, she had been terribly, fantastically pleased to win. She had won without any effort, except to look as nice as possible, and it had given her a different view of herself. She had triumphed for what she was, rather than for what she had done.

She had often reached this conclusion before, but it seemed simplistic and did not quite satisfy her.

Then other thoughts started to drift into her mind as she swam. She had been watching a wonderful series of programmes about Polynesia on television. Not only were the facts interesting but the filming was very fine and Lydia was enthralled with the loveliness of the people and the scenery. She had always enjoyed reading adventure stories of the South Seas. It would have surprised her friends to know how the studious Lydia fantasised about the charming scoundrels, the girls disguised as boys and the buried treasure as portrayed in the works of H de Vere Stacpoole, that under-rated author who describes those beautiful far-away islands and lagoons so vividly. As she watched the colour and the exotic richness of the scenes each week, her mind was filled with a forgotten restlessness. Could a fortnight's holiday allay that restlessness? Could she find a way of pursuing her career in that watery side of the world? Did she really want to uproot herself and leave behind her successful and organised life in Glasgow ?

Lydia finished her swim and with a word here and there to her friends, dressed herself in her elegant grey suit and restored her hair to its usual perfection.

Regretfully she declined to join the "gang" for a drink and left the club.

Outside, in Arlington Street, her dark green car was parked ready to drive her back to the South side.

When Lydia had unlocked the three locks on her front door and greeted Rosa, her enthusiastc striped cat, she toasted some cheese for herself. Then, after sharing a small tin of Nestle's condensed milk with Rosa, she seated herself at the old desk where she would work until midnight and, with the help of her computer, solve some knotty statistical problems.

The Cooling Room

IF YOU BUMPED INTO ME in the street, I expect you would judge me to be an old bird who likes a cigarette, plays bridge, enjoys a G and T and who is happier on the golf course than in the boudoir. And you would be absolutely right. That is a pretty fair picture of me as I am nowadays. But twenty years ago, it was another story altogether. Then my hair was long, straight and dark and my floral, ankle-length Laura Ashley skirt was three sizes smaller than the Marks and Sparks jogging pants that I now wear. Though I was in my forties, I was still amazingly girlish-looking, photographs will prove that. That's not to say I was happier than I am now. Oh no, definitely not. I was a different person and an emotional one in the middle of a lot of other emotional people.

It was the seventies, our three childen were struggling unhappily through their teens and our marriage was pretty rocky. Everyone's marriage was pretty rocky.

It was the era of Feminism and the "Me Generation" when it was the fashionable thing "to find oneself". I seem to remember that it was mostly husbands who were trying to find themselves. It is such a hoot, that idea of finding oneself, as if there were one tiny true personality hiding within each breast which only needed to be winkled out in order to achieve a smooth life of perfect happiness. But, when I look back, I have been *dozens* of people, several personalities often existing simultaneously. Of course they all had their problems but they also had their high points and my memories would be much less rich and satisfying, had I remained constant to some imaginary "true self". Life is so much more adventurous than that, isn't it ? Though I suspect that I may have at last settled to a steady and boring existence, I am glad I can ponder on those glimpses of past turmoil, which seem so necessary a part of the human condition. As I said before, I was a different person twenty years ago and though my waistline was trimmer, the emotional problems were something I should not wish to encounter again.

It is hard to recall just how stressful each day was at that time what with the boys rebelling and disagreeing with every remark that I made and my husband's depression and self-questioning. My very best friend Sylvia was in the middle of a marriage break-up and was in a hideous financial position and another old friend Jane was going through an early menopause. My mother was struggling with her ancient mother, while my Father was drinking seriously, thereby avoiding all the family problems. Creating a few more of his own in fact. Honestly I was afraid to answer the telephone in case I heard another cry for "Help".

In the brief moments when I was not dealing with the pain and dissatisfactions of others I discovered my first grey hairs and a beastly little roll of flesh around my waist. It was the first time that it had struck me that I might not always be the sprightly young woman that I considered myself. It was a chilling realisation, and I could discuss it with no one.

It was around this time that my husband, for some inexplicable reason, decided I should join the Arlington Baths Club. The boys had all been members since they were little but because of the segregation of the sexes they had always gone with their dad and now went by themselves straight from school. George had been a member for yonks, since a child I suppose, and was awfully keen on his club. He went regularly three and four times each week. It didn't seem to do much for his peace of mind, but then he might have been worse without it and frankly I appreciated having him out of the house. In his absence, the children and I spent hours having deep philosophical or ethical discussions in which they would contradict every statement that I made. We were either discussing or screaming at each other. As George seemed uninclined to join either situation, and who can blame him, it really was preferable to have him out of the house.

Against my better judgment, I was persuaded by George to join the Arlington Baths and each Thursday evening I would trot along to the club, but not being a great swimmer and not knowing anyone there made it more of a duty than a pleasure. I suppose it was good for me to get away from the family and the telephone with its dismal callers and I enjoyed the luxurious hot showers and relaxing in the Turkish suite but I found the rules and regulations irksome. I rediscovered the shyness which had plagued me as a schoolgirl and while various members smiled kindly at me, no one seemed willing to start a conversation. Somehow as a new member I felt that it was not up to me. Besides, what was the use of belonging to the same club as your husband and sons if you could never use the facilities at the same time as they did?

I decided that one year would be long enough to remain a member.

As it happened I left even sooner.

This is the story of why I left the club after only five months' membership and also the story of what was probably the last manifestation of romance and excitement in my life. And please do not think for a moment that I have any regrets that it was the last manifestation. Oh dear no. Rather than "Romance", give me a pack of cards and three good bridge players any day.

Where shall I start this sordid tale? I can speak about it quite calmly now and I think it was important to me. I doubt if George and I would still be together, if it had not happened. We were both dissatisfied with the marriage and ready to rush off in our separate ways which would have been a financial disaster for us and possibly an emotional disaster for the boys. Look at what happened to poor Sylvia.

At that time the Arlington had just celebrated its hundredth anniversary, (honestly you would not find this difficult to believe if you visited it), with various events which had been quite successful, and the committee which runs the club decided to continue this social side, probably with the aim of recruiting new members from spouses and friends. They are always pretty desperate to have new members and swell the coffers for the never-ending repairs which are required for the poor old joint. There had been a Burns' Supper but I had said a firm "No" to that. I ask you, haggis and poetry for a whole evening. Just not my scene, I'm afraid. But three months later a party was arranged with a disco for the junior members and general jollifications, mainly wine and cheese, for the adults. The boys, still in their early teens, were partly revolted and partly fascinated by the idea of a disco and allowing themselves to be persuaded to go, though grudgingly, we went *en famille.*

In spite of some excesses, the seventies did give a girl a chance to wear bright pretty clothes. None of the boring black that predominates at parties now, but ankle-length, drifting, diaphanous dresses and long hair worn loose and wild and though I referred to it all mockingly as the "Fairy Princess Syndrome" I enjoyed it as much as the next female. I made myself as attractive as I could that night and George, as always, was generous with his praise for my appearance and even the boys whistled when they saw me.

Athough there was a lot of tension between George and myself that night, which could have developed in various ways, we suppressed it as best we could.

On arrival the boys immediately left us and disappeared in the direction of the music and were not seen again until it was time to go home. The Arlington was unrecognisable with balloons and streamers and the distant strains of the disco, though I never quite found out where that was located. I must say it was a bizarre environment for a party. The brightly dressed crowds clustered dangerously around the calm pool and were reflected picturesquely in the water. But I could visualize, only too clearly, the bedraggled state of anyone unlucky enough to stumble and take an unexpected dip in the water which was so very close to our feet. As the night wore on and more alcohol was consumed, this possibility grew more likely.

George introduced me to several friends and I felt that he was relaxing and starting to enjoy himself. One of the friends was Rupert who had a beard and looked a bit of a desperado. I have always been attracted to desperadoes and as he had a blonde girlfriend and George has always been attracted to blondes the four of us stayed together.

George and Amy, the blonde, talked about swimming and various Olympic champions and their strong and weak points, the sort of conversation that I find paralysingly boring. However Rupert and I had a terrific time and found that we could make each other laugh. By nine o'clock as well as bemoaning the horribly well-behaved days of our youth, we had composed several unprintable limericks and, no doubt, our immoderate laughter drew the attention of others. I do think that a shared sense of humour must be the greatest aphrodisiac. I really had a very good time and shed all my worries for a few hours.

At the end of the evening, which was so much better than I had expected, we collected three dazed but happy little boys. They were most enthusiastic about the disco and some girls who were all called Betty and were "terrific dancers".

George had enjoyed the party too and the stress seemed to have disappeared between us although we did not have much to say to each other.

Next day Rupert phoned and said that he wanted to see me again!

I was absolutely astonished, flattered, excited. You name it. I was bowled over.

Nothing like that had ever happened to me before.

Of course I said "No!" I said I was married, a mother all the rest of it etc etc.

And yet when I hung up I was elated and could not stop smiling in a silly adolescent way. One hour later I was kicking myself for being so prudent and moral and timid.

When he phoned the following day I agreed to meet him in Byres Road for coffee at 2pm. You can judge how strong-minded I am!

Every weekday for three weeks we met in the French tearoom at 2pm. For the first week he insisted on buying us each a huge cream cake and we would gaze into each other's eyes as we ate, just like in a French film. It was corny but enjoyably sensuous. But I had to put a stop to that when on the first Saturday I could not fasten the zip on my jeans.

Rupert was terribly attractive in his hairy way. He had lovely teeth and his use of language and word-play was brilliant. Poor George's sense of humour consists in ponderously relaying a joke which he has heard at the office or perhaps producing a well-known catch phrase at an appropriate moment, but Rupert was much more subtle and original and could make me smile or sometimes guffaw in a very un-tearoom-like manner. After the laughter would come the long looks of unmistakable intensity.

"When can I see you in the evening?" he would whisper through his silky beard and stroke my hand with his hairy paw.

Such hot-house desire, such unrequited yearning was something I had not experienced for sixteen years and it was heady, oh yes it was heady. It was just what I required to remind myself that I was a Woman. Not a wife or mother, charwoman or cook. A Woman!

But I resisted. Certainly I turned up each day for my coffee but I would not commit myself to more. Was I afraid? Did I have the energy for such an intrigue? Because I knew it took energy, organisation and lots of lying to conduct an affair. And I am such a bad liar. I'm hopeless. Then most of my energy was required elsewhere by the practicalities of my demanding family. And surely this would be the coffin nail in our matrimonial situation. I had never remotely considered having an affair before this and the concept was completely alien to me.

Still, might it be just what I needed in order to find myself?

Like a lot of other people at that time, my moral sense seemed to be on sabbatical leave and I had obviously forgotten the high ethical stance that I always held in discussions with my sons.

As the fourth week approached Rupert made it clear that thirty-five minutes of coffee, laughter and langorous glances was not enough, With great dignity and even greater regret I decided to break the whole thing off. What a little prude I was. Nowadays, as I watch the explicit shenanigans on television and marvel at the apparently accepted sexual behaviour of our time, I blush a little for the queenly speech that I made. Rupert took it very well and we parted with a gentle kiss on each cheek, but there were tears in my eyes as I walked home along Highburgh Road.

On the following Thursday, I arrived at the Arlington for my swim at seven o'clock, as usual. To my astonishment, Rupert was standing in the foyer reading the noticeboard. It was so unexpected to see a man on the premises at all on a Ladies night, but I was thrilled to see him and my first thought was that he had come to "carry me off". However he explained that it was an extraordinary meeting of the Arlington committee which he must attend. I was surprised and a little hurt to find that he was a committee member. It showed how little I really knew of his life.

"Meet me afterwards," he muttered huskily so close to my ear that his beard tickled my neck.

"I don't think I can. Where? When ?" I replied or some equally incoherent statement.

"Here or no, in the boot hall . No, in the cooling room, after everyone has gone, after ten or so."

"How could we do that?" I asked inanely. I expect my mouth was open.

The cooling room, I should explain, is the large dim room where members can recline and relax after the vicissitudes of a

Turkish bath or a massage. It is furnished with seventeen sheet-draped armchairs and a weighing machine, while against the wall, behind curtains similar to those which are pulled around hospital beds, are two banquettes and, for the truly exhausted, two small divans, two very small divans. It was never my favourite place as it was usually crowded with well-established chattering groups in the evening and after peeping in once or twice, my shyness made me avoid it completely. And Rupert was suggesting that we met there in the crowds! But of course they would all have left by ten.

I felt confused but also excited. I was reminded of the improvisations that my English teacher would give us in school. She would take four or five pupils and give each of us a short character description and then suggest a situation that we might find ourselves in. I thoroughly enjoyed acting it out and had quite a knack for exaggerating my character and complicating the whole issue. As we improvised, I would forget my shyness and it was really fun. This present situation seemed to have the same sense of unreality and potential for danger.

Just then two men walked in the front door and Rupert touched my arm, smiling meaningfully then joined the others as they went upstairs, where the meeting was to be held presumably.

I told myself firmly that this was not an improvisation and I must keep a cool head. I should really just go home right away. But of course I didn't. I cannot remember showering or swimming or drying my hair though I suppose I did all of those things. I did go into the Turkish room quite late and sit and lie there in a state of indecision for about an hour. I dreaded entering the cooling room with its unwelcoming cliques but I was relieved to find only three ladies still relaxing there at half-past nine and I was able to pick up a magazine and settle myself unobtrusively in an armchair. Gradually the room emptied completely. Then I wondered if the staff would come to check whether everyone had left or not. I did not see how I could avoid leaving if I were asked outright to go. I decided to pull the curtain around one of the divans then lie down and pretend to be asleep. If an attendant came along that would seem innocent enough. I gulped as I thought how devious I was becoming. Strategy and skullduggery are not my metier in life. It is surprising to me now that I did not worry or manufacture excuses about returning home so very late, but George and the children had melted from my consciousness.

The time passed and the place became quieter and quieter. I lay on my hard litttle divan and wondered what time it was. I was wrapped only in one of the large sheets, that is *de rigeur* for the cooling room and my bare shoulders were becoming chilly. I sat up. It was a bit ridiculous lying here waiting and freezing. I suddenly thought of a cup of coffee and how nice it would be to have one to warm my hands. I imagined myself in my warm red kaftan sitting in my own comfy chair at home with a cup of coffee and I leaped to my feet, determined to go home at once. Just at that moment the swing door of the cooling room slowly creaked open and Rupert entered with a conspiratorial air. It is ridiculous, but I remember being a little shocked that he still wore his outdoor shoes, as they are supposed to be removed in the boot hall and are forbidden in any of the inner sanctums of the club.

"I'm sorry to be so long, did you think I wouldn't *ever* get here, my darling. The bar took such a time to empty and I had to hang around until no one was left that would ask awkward questions. *Isn't this deliciously exciting?*" and he gathered me up in his arms tenderly.

To be perfectly honest, I would have been happy to go home to that vision of kaftan and coffee which I had just conjured in my mind, but as has often been the case in my overly-polite life I saw no way out of the situation at that particular moment.

Unlike those modern novels which we all read on planes, I have no intention of giving a detailed account of our night of love in the cooling room, suffice it to say that the room was *very well named*. As the night wore on, not only did the temperature drop considerably but our passions cooled to sub-zero. The divan was unbelievably cramped for two long-legged people and even the ten sheets which we collected at different times throughout the night from the armchairs, were not sufficient to keep us warm. At one point we separated to the two divans and it was good to stretch but I soon became frozen and returned to Rupert's embrace. It did not occur to us to leave the building. Anyway I expect we were securely locked in. It was without doubt the longest, coldest and most uncomfortable night of my life and it was almost a relief to hear the sharp business-like footsteps of the bathsmaster the next morning at six-thirty. He was whistling as he pushed open the swing doors but he stopped in the middle of a bar.

"What the bloody blazes...!" he exclaimed, as he saw the sheetless armchairs, I suppose. Then his hesitant footsteps approached the back of the room and with a sharp jerk he dragged back the curtains around our little corner and for a moment was unable to speak. It must have given the poor fellow quite a shock when I think of it and I am sorry about that.

It must have appeared to him that we were in *flagrante delicto* but in fact we were only huddled together to keep warm.

"Good God!" he exclaimed roughly "I don't want to know anything about this. You'd better get your clothes on and get to hell out of here as quick as you can."

Then he turned on his heel and left us. He was very, very angry but I think he behaved in a gentlemanly way and I shall always be grateful to him.

I had to return to the changing cubicle in the dim pool hall where I had left my clothes but I was glad of the darkness and I have never dressed myself so quickly. In a few moments Rupert and I met in the foyer and exchanged a polite kiss then left as quickly as possible and drove off to our respective homes just as the morning traffic was starting to move in the city. It was the end of our brief affair and I had no regrets whatever because I had learned something important that night. Rupert adoring desperado that he seemed and as excitingly hairy as a grizzly bear, could not compare with my husband. Good old George, stressed out and exhausted on a Friday night, could still generate more tenderness and imagination than Rupert dreamed of, bless him.

Imagination is so important, I think.

How I did enjoy a cup of coffee in my kitchen before George stumbled downstairs at eight o'clock. As we sleep in twin beds and as I am always up first anyway and he is pretty dopey in the morning, George did not notice that I had not been to bed that night, strange though it may seem. That was one of the problems solved at any rate.

Of course I never did return to the Arlington Baths, though Rupert is still a member, still on the committee after all these years and I think that says a lot about his personality! He has shaved off his beard now and we sometimes see each other in the distance and exchange a small half-hearted wave. But as I said, I have never gone back to the club. I could not have looked the bathsmaster in the eye again for one thing and I could not have taken pleasure in the facilities, too full of embarrasing memories. I never did enjoy getting wet so very much anyway!

George is still an enthusiastic club member. I do not know if he ever discovered anything about that night, but he has never mentioned it and neither have I. We are still together and will celebrate our thirty-seventh anniversary next month. George was keen to hire the function suite at the Arlington for our "do" but I persuaded him that a hotel would be better. We don't have to worry about the pennies now as quite soon after that night in the cooling room my poor old grandmother died, releasing my mother from her slavery and leaving a surprisingly large amount of cash. Mother was enabled to say cheerio to my difficult dad and to open the little antique shop she had always dreamed of. My share of the legacy eased the family finances and removed some of the furrows from George's brow and also bought me my own little car. Quite soon I joined Hilton Park golf course where, forty years previously, my grandmother had been captain. You can see her name in gold on the wooden plaque in the dining room. I suppose I started to golf to show my gratitude to Granny but I love it and find I have quite a talent for it and I expect to be elected vice-captain next year.

On Tuesday and Thursday nights George and I play bridge and we are both *very* keen and not bad players at all I must admit.

The boys are all grown up, married and earning reasonable salaries and we have four granddaughters, who are very sweet after all those boisterous boys.

If I ever think of my brief affair nowadays, I have to say that the cream cakes and the langorous glances in the Patisserie Francaise were the best of it.

Yes, I suppose that George and I are quite a Darby and Joan really and in spite of my golf, his swimming and our bridge, he is seldom exhausted nowadays and he is still a most imaginative man.

I do think imagination is so important.

The Baths in the 1940s

IN 1944 WHEN I WAS TWELVE I was delighted to return to my home town of Glasgow. My mother and I had been living in my grandparents' holiday house in the East coast fishing village of Pittenweem since the outbreak of war and for me it had not been a happy experience. The spoilt and rather sophisticated town child that I suppose I was at seven was unwelcome in that insular and suspicious small community. My wider general knowledge and vocabulary, though probably appreciated by the teachers, did not boost my popularity with the other pupils in the class and my clothes and my accent were derided in the streets. I was lonely and sometimes miserable and I missed and longed for the stimulating life which I had always known in Glasgow. My existence in Pittenweem seemed very simple and boring but though I did not realise it, many of my fantasies were of a life in pre-war Glasgow and of a situation which no longer existed.

I would remember sitting on a rocking horse while having my hair cut in the big department store of Copland and Lye. That might be followed by a modestly-priced and delicious lunch of stewed sweetbreads in their restaurant where a trio of sedate ladies in black played familiar tunes from light opera. Or perhaps we would just pop in to Copland's Coffee Room some afternoon, to drink Russian tea served in a tall glass tumbler held in a silver cage. I loved to watch the slice of lemon moving gently in the hot golden liquid like some underwater creature. The waitresses always remembered my favourite delicacy and if we were later than usual there might have to be a search of all the tables to locate "a pineapple cake for wee Nanzie". Someone was always successful and would thread their way across the tearoom with a big smile, holding aloft the three-tier cake-stand in triumph.

Sometimes we would visit that most wonderful of all emporiums, Lewis's Polytechnic, always referred to in our family as the Poly. Its escalators were unique in Glasgow at that time, as far as I know. That was one of the things about Glasgow which I learned never to mention in Pittenweem as the very idea of a moving staircase was greeted by hoots of indignant disbelief and unconcealed brow-pointing in reference to my doubtful sanity.

Lewis's had a vast food department on the ground floor. As well as cheese, meat and fish counters there were all the delicious smells of the bakery and the delicatessen. There were often introductory "samples" to try. Tiny slices of cheese or little cardboard cups of soup were appealing to a child because of their miniature size and astonishingly they were also free! The Polly was the first place that I tasted Coca-cola, which I found disappointing after the years of wonderful advertisements that I had gazed at in the National Geographic magazines. It was the only place that I ever sampled a slice of pineapple dipped in chocolate, but that was not a great success. The toy department in this enormous store was also breathtaking for a child, especially at the different festivals. At Christmas there were moving tableaux in the windows which seemed more spectacular than the present day equivalent in spite of the electronic aids now available but perhaps that only reflects the innocence and ignorance of my youth. Inside jolly little elves helped Santa Claus in his grotto. I particularly remember one Easter when a little bridge led over a pool of real water with real daffodils and real ducks with their real fluffy ducklings. I was enchanted. I cannot say why it was so very much more exciting than the duckpond in Kelvingrove Park, but it was.

The top floor of the Polly was the best of all, because there a strong aroma announced the large pet shop and zoo in which was the white parrot which, I theorised, gave the store its friendly name. None of the adults in my life discredited the idea when I spoke of it. As a child I liked explanations and I held various theories each probably based on a similarly shaky premise. The large cages also housed puppies and kittens, rabbits and guinea pigs, snakes, tortoises and monkeys and from what she said, I guessed that my mother yearned for a monkey.

Apart from the Polly, there were elegant tearooms which we visited regularly, where immense and richly coloured stained glass windows appealed to me especially. Then we went at least once a week to the Kelvingrove Art Galleries which had a plethora of fascinating objects, unlimited stuffed animals, models of dinosaurs, medieval Japanese armour, Red Indian moccasins, African masks, beautiful paintings, life-like sculptures and pieces of machinery that worked at the touch of a button. Then there were the many models of ships of all sizes which particularly fascinated me. I would people their decks with tiny sailors. What very patient adults must have accompanied me as I stood and gazed and thought and imagined. I expect it was usually my adoring Grandfather who shepherded me through the vast halls and enriched the visits with background facts and stories. I found the space of the Galleries delightful and the marble floors and sweeping staircases satisfied that desire for living in a castle which I suspect all children harbour.

No, although the narrow wynds and stony beaches of Pittenweem had their own attraction, they could not compare with those lost city pleasures and by far the biggest loss for me was my thrice-weekly visit to the Arlington Baths. How very much I missed swimming. Of course I could swim in the sea throughout the brief weeks of summer but then, for the rest of the year, there was no indoor swimming pool nearer than Dundee or Dunfermline, both impossibly far away in those non car-owning days. How I longed for the warmth and familiarity of the pool which had been part of my life as long as I could remember.

As I have said already, the decision was taken in 1944 to return to Glasgow and like most people, until they learn from experience, I saw this change as an absolute end to all my worries and the start of a happy interesting life full of loving friends and pleasant days.

My home was in a West End tenement but a great deal of my life was spent in the Charing Cross area where I was enrolled at the Glasgow High School for Girls, in Garnethill. My Grandparents' house was at 351 Renfrew Street and I had lunch with them on alternate weeks as at that time school lunches were restricted. I attended ballet class each Saturday morning at the Charing Cross school run by Margaret Hopkins, that unsung Glasgow doyenne of dance. And religiously, on Tuesdays and Thursdays after school, I walked along Woodlands Road to my dear Arlington baths club and swam until the whistle was blown to clear the pool of juniors at six o'clock.

Of course Glasgow was dirty and noisy and smelly compared to Pittenweem. I had rather forgotten about that and it was a shock. Apart from the Belisha beacon crossings, which were unsafe and few and far between, there was no help for the pedestrian who wished to cross the street. After five years of strolling along the middle of the road in Fife, it was a nightmare for me to cross the intersection at Charing Cross what with tram cars hurtling back and forth from several directions, buses swinging around the corner, horse-drawn carts and terrifyingly fast motor cars, though admittedly only a few of the last. Even the pavements seemed dangerous with hurrying figures who crowded me to the kerb and bumped into me without a word of apology. Although we are fond of saying how fast the pace of life is now, I think that pedestrians move more slowly now. Perhaps they have better clothing to keep them warm, perhaps they have fewer deadlines. There are fewer of them too, as I suppose that more are in cars. Nowadays I think one has to go into town on a Saturday close to Christmas to experience the hustling, crowding, intimidating throng, which I remember from my childnood.

Nevertheless I was deliriously happy to be back.

I often ran errands for my grandmother and was familiar with all the shops in the Charing Cross area. I would collect her grocery rations from the imposing establishment of Cooper's which was a few minutes walk along Sauchiehall street to the east. Even in those straitened times this long-established Glasgow firm, which had several other magnificent branches in the city, managed to permeate the street outside its premises with an enticing smell of coffee. Inside, it was necessary to stand in several queues for the various different items.There was a separate counter for bacon, another for butter and cheese and another for sugar, biscuits and dried goods, which made shopping there a lengthier process than at any other shop that I had ever come across. I found it irksome, I admit, but was always fascinated by the last counter where paper bags, boxes and tins were painstakingly and perfectly wrapped into a large smooth parcel. How did they squash all those disparate nobbly shapes into a sharply rectangular parcel and where did all that brown paper and string come from in those days of austerity? I was relieved when my grandmother transferred her custom to Massey's which was nearer and quicker, though I realised it did not have quite the status of Cooper's.

On the road to Cooper's I would pass Lyon's stationery emporium. In its window were wonderful leather goods, attache and brief cases, diaries, purses, handbags and elegant folders to hold envelopes and writing paper, the last being a hotshot favourite birthday present in those days. I expect that a large proportion of all twenty-first birthday presents was bought in Lyon's. All wedding invitations and mourning stationery was available there too and around the corner, in Elmbank Street, was a side-window, where charming stuffed toys were on view, but that may have been in later years.

Across the road from Lyons was the long and very steep hill which the girls of the Glasgow High School climbed each day. It has a daunting aspect but I never remember noticing that it was especially punishing except when it was occasionally snowy and slippy. As I was often *en retard* I expect that I went up the hill at a fast trot. Little wonder that the ex-pupils of the High School are a stoic and sturdy bunch.

Returning to Charing Cross from that hill I passed the Beresford Hotel, which I know now to be a fine example of Art Deco architecture. I always did think it very smart and like something in a film, though I expect its frontage was grubby in those days compared to its present immaculate facade. Everything was pretty grubby in those days, including the girls of the High School after a day in town.

Close to that was Mackinley's book shop, which stocked the text books and jotters with which we were required to provide ourselves at the High School. There was a great shortage of text books and the word would go around the class when some long-awaited book had arrived at Mackinley's. I seldom carried enough money to buy one that day and I was also a forgetful child. With only a few copies available I, alas, was often too late to acquire the book and no doubt some of my subjects suffered as a result. I was certainly no longer the queen of the class which I had been in the small village school. I cannot remember that it worried me too much and I soon assumed the role of court jester. A day in which I did not reduce my friends to helpless giggles was a day wasted.

Next door to the book-shop was a most quaint "boutique" selling elaborate sweaters. It was a most unlikely little establishment, with a small unchanging stock and no apparent customers. I mention it because it stayed in business longer than any of its neighbours. Its window always had seven or eight bright jumpers with bobbles and flowers knitted in or sewn on. None of my friends ever had a sweater like that and I never met any one else wearing one and yet that shop seemed to me to continue offering its bobbly, flowery, sweaters to the public for the next thirty-odd years but perhaps I am mistaken, though it was there for a very long time.

Then there was the vast Locarno ballroom, the haunt at

that time of tall gum-chewing American forces. To a school-girl there was an air of sex and wickedness about it and I always walked past quickly with only a sideways glimpse for any sign of day-time depravity. Generally speaking, High School girls tended to the prudish.

There was a cinema at Charing Cross, the King's at which it was always possible to see films which you had missed when they had been first released. Some were really old. In the days before TV and videos it was quite difficult to catch a film if one had missed it in the first few months, unless you went to a cinema in some small rural area. For instance, Pittenweem Picture House had been a gold-mine of ancient and unknown films. Outside the King's cinema, two large angels stood guard and still do stand there although the building itself has metamorphosed many times in fifty years, not always respectably. From espresso coffee bar to Chinese restaurant, to blue movie salon and gambling casino the history of the King's would make a social comment on fifty years of fashions in entertainment. I can clearly remember the long narrow auditorium of this small cinema and several of the films that I saw there. In my teens, some school friends and I watched a version of "Lorna Doone", hoping that it might enable us to pass a forthcoming test, as none of us had found time to read the original book. Such is the optimism of youth. I also saw "King Kong" in that same cinema, probably before the war. It made a terrific impression on me and I do not find it surprising that it has become such a cult movie. Also before the war I watched that best disaster movie of all time "San Francisco", in which Jeannette Macdonald, in immaculate evening dress, wanders through the life-like devastation of the 1906 earthquake. That film gave me a deep terror of earthquakes and at the same time a great desire to visit San Francisco, though I have experienced neither. I also fell in love for the first time in that cinema, when the gorgeous young Don Ameche, disguised as Alexander Graham Bell, invented the telephone.

Around the corner in St George's Road was another cinema,

the Crystal Palace, It was owned by one of Glasgow's eccentrics, A.E. Pickard. who owned property throughout the city and was not shy about advertising his ownership with large posters in the windows of his empty and dilapidated buildings. But this cinema was a most luxurious establishment with delightfully comfortable seats though the mirror-lined walls of the auditorium reflected the screen many times in a way that I certainly found disconcerting. I can remember seeing Chaplin's "Great Dictator" in that theatre. As a young child I had taken great delight in watching the magnificent model of the Forth Bridge which the whimsical Mr Pickard had constructed on the roof, high above the entrance. As I was used to crossing the Forth Bridge on our journeys to Fife I felt a great personal interest and possessiveness about this model and no doubt kept my accompanying adult waiting, while I watched for the little lighted train to make its way across the bridge several times. The train was not running in the forties, of course, but the sight of the bridge still pleased me.

Then there was Woolworths which, though sparsely-stocked, had always some interesting little item for a few pennies. I remember buying a small papier-mache party hat which would look just like a lady's on my favourite doll. I had not quite discarded my doll-dressing at twelve. I also bought a white cream-jug and sugar-bowl and with some tiny tins of enamel from a hard-ware store in George's road, attempted to create a special Christmas present for my mother. Though perhaps not completely successful, as the enamel remained sticky for the next twenty years, I know that the present was appreciated and treasured.

In the 1940s, Ross's dairy at Charing Cross had what we would now call a snack-bar and my mother and I often popped in there. There was a shelf running around two of the walls with high stools to sit on, just as they did in American films and I thought it very dashing to perch on a stool, with my knees just showing beneath my skirt and drink a glass of milk and nibble a ham roll with mustard. I must also mention a larger Ross's dairy which was situated a few blocks nearer to the city centre. It had a restaurant with chairs and tables and served proper, if scant, meals though we hardly ever patronised this branch. What it did have was a bakery, open to the public view in a side window, where one could watch a deft and speedy lady mixing, rolling, cutting and baking magnificent and incredible quantities of girdle scones, enough scones to satisfy the Glasgow masses. With an echo of the supreme dealing skill of the card-sharp, soda, treacle and potato scones were laid out in serried ranks on a hotplate as big as a large kitchen table. No sooner was the last corner of the hotplate covered, than it was time to return to the first scone and turn them all over with a quick and peculiar flick. I had watched this process from early childhood, as long as those patient adults would allow me. At home, when much younger, I had gathered together as many gloves as possible and, substituting them for scones, practised the skills of laying and flicking-over with assiduity. Though there was not the continuous production in the forties that there had been in pre-war days, there were still occasions when I could watch and envy that busy young woman, possibly only a couple of years older than myself, in her neat white apron and head-band.

Just about every article could be purchased in or around Charing Cross at that time. Malcolm Campbell's fruit and vegetables and Sawyer's fish shop, Boots the chemist and one or two other chemists. There was a rather empty draper's shop, a jeweller, a hardware store and several of the large and elegant Glasgow bakeries still thrived though I suspect that their once-busy tearooms were closed "for the duration", which was a phrase much in use at that time. There were shoe shops, dress shops and even furriers. I cannot think that they had much in the way of merchandise to offer in those war years but most of them seemed to struggle on and there was a brave elegance in many of the Sauchiehall Street shop-windows that impressed me tremendously after five years of the Pittenweem High Street. There were many hairdressers and beauty parlours in the area, fascinating and sophisticated to a teenager. Mary London, Girault and Bambers. As well as hairdessing, Bambers was a theatrical costumiers and rented out exotic and elaborate fancy dress, which was displayed tastefully in their window with various wigs, though I am not sure how much business they would do in those days of general hardship. Around the corner in Renfrew Street, Bambers owned or rented one of the main-door flats of Albany Mansions, the block in which my Grandparents lived. Bambers untenanted flat was used for storage only and must have been a thorn in the flesh of the inhabitants of that luxurious building as it was always neglected and filthy with ancient broken-down cardboard boxes pressing pathetically against the dirty windows. In fact, Renfrew Street was generally a run-down place at that time, with low-grade boarding houses, theatrical digs and no doubt several houses of ill-repute. Albany Mansions with its swing doors, marble stairways and spacious flats was a little island of middle-class respectability. The stately red-sandstone tenements had been designed in the 1890s by Burnet and, as it had been suggested to him that there was a dearth of accommodation for artists in Glasgow, he had used the top floor and the attics to create a superb flat suitable for a successful artist. I think that the need for an artist's flat throws an interesting light on the cultural scene in Glasgow at that time. With a large two-storey studio for entertaining buyers, "sitters" and for the occasional exhibition and another atelier in the remaining attic space, for the messy real work, it was a wonderful home for an artist and his family. My grandfather had acquired the flat in 1911 and had pursued his excellent career there. It was a magical house for a child and on returning to it from my exile in Fife I rediscovered things which I had begun to believe might only exist in my imagination. The L-shaped atelier had a Dutch stove, a printing press, a life-size lay figure, hundreds of books and of course paintings everywhere and was similar to the attics belonging to romantic Parisian artists about which one read in books or saw depicted in films.

I felt that I was so lucky to have the freedom to explore this studio that belonged to my own grandfather, with whom I had always had such a special relationship.

On Tuesdays and Thursdays I attended the Arlington Baths, as I have said. We left school at three-thirty on a Thursday so that was a bonus. My friend Olive, a beautiful girl in my class, and I were both members of the Arlington and twice a week we walked together from school, down Hill Street and Renfrew Street and then along Woodlands Road to the baker's shop which stood at the top of Arlington street. I think that sometimes we would have money for a little cake and sometimes not. I remember that there was never much selection by that time in the afternoon, perhaps if we were lucky we might still find a "piney cake" with pineapple jam and ersatz cream or a "fern cake" with a stylised fern scribbled on the white icing. More likely we would find only coconut-encrusted "Eiffel Towers" or the dry-as-dust Paris buns, whose only enchantment was a sprinkling of sugar crystals.

Olive was a willowy and rather stern brunette with marvellous eyes and carriage. We were not particular friends although we ran with the same "pack". Some girls found Olive intimidating and have admitted to feeling afraid of her, which certainly seems ridiculous now when one thinks of the charming and kind lady that she is today. I was rather shy of her perhaps and I was certainly proud that she deigned to accompany me, for although I had never felt at home in the country school, neither did I find it easy to find my niche in the sophisticated city school, with its middle-class conventions and snobberies, both material and intellectual. Olive and I became very good friends in that year that we swam together every week. There is nothing like swimming to generate a close friendship.

It was always very quiet in the Arlington when we went there. It seems to me that often we were the only people on the premises. Occasionally we had glimpses of a member of staff or perhaps a lone elderly member, wrapped in a sheet and shuffling in slippers, making her way to the Turkish. Once or twice a few other young girls arrived and made a commotion, but that was rare. Generally we had everything to ourselves. Our two pairs of shoes would be the only ones under the bench in the boot hall, our clothes were the only clothes hanging in the junior changing room and the shower room was dry until we used it.

I have to admit that Olive and I spent quite a lot of our time in the delicious warm water of the showers and made a fair amount of noise in that small echoing chamber. What with animal impersonations and songs which were accompanied by a tattoo beaten on the marble partitions between the shower-stalls (I remember that the "Volga Boat Song" was a favourite), we were a rowdy pair of representatives of the genteel High School for Girls. What is amazing is that nobody ever came to rebuke us! No one seemed to be there.When we tore ourselves away from the delights of the showers, the pool was ours alone. I cannot think that we were dedicated swimmers. We were so much more ignorant of the possibilities of swimming in those pre-TV days. We liked to jump off the high diving-dail and we tried to swing on the rings. There were two sets of swinging rings in those days but we seemed to be too tall for the transverse rings and not quite tall enough for the others. The trapeze was quite difficult to catch, as the hooked wooden pole to catch it was long and heavy and unwieldy and though I often held the bar of the trapeze in one hand while I clung to the platform support with the other, my courage would then evaporate and I would abort the proceedings and jump into the water. I realise now that it was a lack of application that stopped us from acquiring those swinging skills. Perhaps if we had been able to watch an expert we would have tried harder and succeeded. The ladder leading to the trapeze platform was wooden and I devised a trick of climbing up the underside of this ladder and then launching myself backwards to land in the water with an almighty splash. It was not elegant but it was original and it was fun and we did it quite a lot. After our swim we dressed and climbed the stairs, pausing on the balcony to declaim "Romeo, Romeo, Wherefore art thou, Romeo?" Upstairs, the gymnasium with its gigantic parallel bars and wide range of Indian clubs and antiquated rowing machine was ours alone. What a marvellous time we had there, still young enough to indulge in imaginary games. "Pirates" was a favourite as the rowing machine demanded a nautical theme. Sometimes we fantasised about delicious and unobtainable sweetmeats, creating in our imagination unheard-of delicacies of chocolate, marshmallow and marzipan. Real marzipan, not the nutritious but stolid substitute which was made of soya flour and almond essence, but the true ambrosial ground-almond marzipan which I could just remember as a beautiful dream.

It seems strange to me now but, although we were both well-grown girls of thirteen, I cannot remember that sex or even romance ever formed part of our conversations.

By six o'clock juniors were not supposed to be in the pool hall and although I do not remember being chivvied as I do not remember anyone there to chivvy us, Olive and I would dutifully, though regretfully, retire to the last stage of our visit, the reading room. In those days the reading room was where the bar is now situated. It was welcoming and cheerful with a well-tended, blazing fire, but who tended the fire, I wonder? There were all the daily papers neatly laid on the large central table and on a side-table were the magazines. As well as the Readers' Digest, National Geographic and Punch, there were the Tatler and the Illustrated London News, periodicals unknown outside the Arlington. Olive and I would pore over the photographs of the aristocracy attending dinners and dances and society weddings and giggle at their outfits. I suppose those publications were the forties' equivalent of "Hello" magazine. We would sometimes have a game of draughts or have a look through the "Recent Members" book, always talking in whispers, as a large notice advised silence and we were law-abiding girls.

By six-twenty, it was time for Olive to catch her train and rather than catch my bus in Woodland's Road, I would walk back to Charing Cross with her for another ten minutes of talk. The pangs of hunger were no doubt striking our innards by that time and there was a temptingly odorous chip shop which we must pass so, as it was forbidden to eat in the street while wearing uniform, we would stuff our hats and ties in our school-bags and buy a poke of chips each.

Olive left the club after a year and I too stopped for a while, feeling rather timid about coming on my own. But, encouraged by my mother who was not able to accompany me herself, I soon fell into my regular ways again. As an only child I have never had problems with being alone and while I did not make the same uninhibited howls in the showers as before (and it was probably I who had originally instigated those) I still cavorted in the water and enjoyed the equipment in the dusty gym upstairs. I still invented complicated sweets and admired the brides and debutantes in the Tatler.

I remember noticing things which I had not seen before. The mysterious wooden box in the washroom called, according to my mother, the Russian bath. Many times I was on the point of opening it and taking a seat inside and turning on the steam tap which my mother described, but I thought that I might be discovered and I never quite had the nerve, although there still seemed to be nobody in the building.

At that time a large notice in the washroom proclaimed "NO SOAP IN THE SHOWERS", I suppose in case of accident, so I always washed my hair in one of the washroom basins. When the plug was pulled, the warm soapy water was released right on to the floor and splashed over your bare feet in a very pleasant way. Hair-washing was a more momentous occasion in those days and tended, as far as I was concerned, to happen at fortnightly intervals as my hair was very long and did not dry quickly. The shampoo that I used was a powder which came in a little paper packet and must be dissolved in warm water before use. It was called an Evan Williams Camomile Shampoo for fair hair, I remember. It was possible to dry your hair in the junior changing room at unique and ancient brass contraptions which were permanently fixed in the wall at varying heights. There were five or six of these circular driers, each with a spherical brass cover which opened rather like an eyelid, I always thought. When opened, a blast of warm air flowed from the circular aperture. This was probably diverted from the warm air which maintained the Turkish suite at its Sahara-like temperature. I will not say that those driers were very efficient but then I had never come across an electric hair-drier at that time, although I suppose that they were invented, and the brass "eyelids" were all that we knew.

I was also intrigued by the chute down which I threw my damp towels. I could never quite make out what happened to them though I always peered carefully after them. I also wondered what on earth was the reason for the bubbles of air which created quite a lot of violence in the water at the shallow end. What I adored was the soft, sprinkling "rain shower" which cascaded over the pool on hot summer days presumably to lower the temperature. When the fine spray drifted down on my upturned face I *knew* it was simply *bound* to make me more beautiful. If I let it fall on my shoulders I was reminded of days in the open-air swimming-pool at Pittenweem when a shower of rain seemed to warm the icy water.

Isn't it strange that no matter how happy one is, one's thoughts so often drift to other places and other, possibly less happy, times?

Shortly after finishing the above article, I was speaking to a fellow member, a gentleman renowned for his prowess on the rings and trapeze. On asking him when he had joined the baths, I found that he too, had been a teenage member in the 1940s, along with his fellow boy scouts. As he remembered, his face lit up and he started to describe the scene in the pool when the boys arrived and it could not have been more different from my tranquil memories. He pictured for me queues of boys lining up at the foot of each trapeze-ladder awaiting their turn, while crowds jostled for a "shot" at either end of each set of rings and a continuous stream of lads leaped or dived from the high diving dale into a pool which seethed with bodies. His vivid description explained the invisibility of staff that I remembered on my Tuesday and Thursday visits. Staff members would obviously be taking the opportunity to recuperate and recruit their strength in order to deal with the maelstrom of small flying boys who would return to invade the premises every Monday, Wednesday and Friday!

I asked my fellow member if he had ever had a fortnight's suspension, a punishment which my dare-devil father received regularly when a boy, I believe.

"A fortnight!" he exclaimed, "Oh, often! and sometimes a month and once I was up before the committee."

As he spoke, the emotion of delight was clear upon his brow and not a shred of shame was visible.

No Harm Done

MY MOTHER SAYS I am always in a hurry and I do seem to be late for everything, no matter how hard I try. Now that I live in a flat, of course, Mum isn't there to find all those little things that you cannot put your hands on at the last minute and I often get into a flap. Somehow the other girls don't seem to have so much trouble finding just the right shoes or gloves or book or whatever it is, perhaps they are not so particular. My problem is that I have so many *things*. Sometimes my flatmates get cross. Jennifer is awfully good at finding what I have lost, she must have that sort of brain, but she does not always do it in a very nice way. She will never help me if I ask her outright and turns abruptly on her heel and walks away in quite a rude manner. I do like her though, I like them all and I think they like me. I often wash the dishes when it isn't even my turn and if I go away anywhere, I always bring a little gift back for each of them. Just some little thing to hang up or keep on the mantel-piece.

My boyfriend laughs at all my disasters and says that they don't matter. He thinks I am like a little timid fluttering bird and he just wants to look after me. I think that is so sweet. When I borrowed his lovely striped shirt and scorched it with the iron, he said that it was an old shirt and he was tired of it anyway. There was the other time too, when I left the food for the picnic on the train and he did look so disappointed when he met me, but I think he really quite enjoys my little calamities. They amuse him.

I have joined the Arlington swimming club just recently.

Jennifer did not think I would like it, but I persuaded her to put me up for membership and I love it. Although I have to admit that I have had some unfortunate experiences in the club, things that were not exactly my fault but they were embarrassing. There was the time in the shower room when I wanted to use a stool that was there and there was a towel on the stool. When I picked up the towel, and I cannot really remember what I was going to do with it, put it somewhere safe I suppose, a lady in a shower yelped,

"That's my towel!" she was so sharp, it gave me a terrible fright and I dropped the towel on the wet floor and then somehow the stool fell over. I don't think the stool touched her toes although it fell quite near her foot but she jumped and howled. I suppose I should have offered to get her another towel but really I was upset and confused by that time and I just hid myself in a shower with my face to the wall.

I must admit I haven't really found the members very friendly.

There is no doubt that catastrophes do follow me around. When I was at home I used to be so unlucky when I was washing dishes. Mum used to smile when I offered to wash up and said that I did not need to if I had home-work, but I like to help. At first I did break one or two things, china is so slippy when it is wet. When there was an accident, mum would laugh and say,

"Don't worry dear, if nobody broke any dishes there would be no need for new china and the factories would close and all those people would be out of work."

It was very comforting and I would always repeat that formula when a dish was broken and Mum would smile. Sometimes it would look as though she was going to add another philosophical remark, but she didn't. Last year, when Dad retired, Mum said that I need never wash dishes at home again as she was sure that I had plenty of dish-washing to do in the flat and anyway it was something that could occupy Dad's spare time. She mumbled something about "chipping a lesser evil" but I didn't quite follow that.

To go back to the baths, I had only been a member for a fortnight when my key-card broke in the lock. Mr B the bathsmaster said that no one had ever broken a card before, but it's only a little piece of plastic, after all. It was a pity that they had to issue a new key-card to each member in the middle of the year, but I didn't realise it would be so fragile and I said I was sorry. Then there was the time that my money stuck in the soft drinks machine, the instructions are rather unclear, don't you think. Oh yes and there was the time that I fell off the rings. I didn't know that I was going to land so near to that old gentleman at the shallow end. I'm only learning and you cannot tell when or where you are going to fall and I think he could have been more understanding when I apologised.

Last Saturday I had a bad day, nothing important, just a lot of little things happened that didn't affect anyone but myself, but it was depressing. I got to the baths early, for once, and when I arrived, there were workmen delivering scaffolding outside the front door. The noise as they threw it down off the lorry was scary, that big metallic thump and clanging was terrifying and I got a bit confused. Perhaps I did go too near to where they were working, but they needn't have been so abusive. It would have been me that would have been injured after all. I'm more used to being whistled at than sworn at by workmen and their language was awful. I managed to insert the key-card the right way for once and was glad to escape into the club but my ears were burning for ages.

Then things started to go really wrong. I found that I had brought Jennifer's swimsuit by mistake! She always swims a mile on a Saturday morning and I hated to think of her searching and searching for her suit, but what could I do? I had a short and uncomfortable swim as she is taller than I am and her costume is far too baggy for me, hardly decent. Then I suppose I could have phoned home but I dreaded telling her that her wet costume was waiting for her at the Arlington. I decided to go straight into town to shop after I left the baths.

I knew that I could explain it all to Jennifer later

Now I must make a little confession. You know how you are only supposed to take one towel and one sheet. Well I have this really, really thick hair and I just cannot get it dry without rubbing it hard with at least three towels. And I always try to find a big sheet in the pile, a well-worn one is best, and I wrap my hair up tightly in that to take out the last of the excess moisture and then it falls into big soft curls. I will say that I have nice hair.

Last Saturday, after my swim, I had gone into the big domed room with the coloured windows for a little while to warm up, and I had even had a shot in the wee extra hot room and I must have left my sheet lying around there somewhere. It was such a nuisance, I was nearly dressed when I discovered that I had no sheet. I never really got my hair right that day. And another thing that had happened in that domed room was that my bottle of aromatherapy oil had tipped over on the floor. I couldn't believe it when I looked down because I was sure that I had put the top on it, but there was a big oily puddle on the floor. I had no tissues to mop it up so I just left it. Fortunately it was in the corner of the room. I expect it would evaporate eventually. Does oil evaporate, I wonder? I expect they wash that floor sometimes, too. Anyway I didn't see what else I could do. It was quite nice stuff too, lavender or rose or something like that. I got it in Boots and it was quite dear. Though to be truthful I don't have much sense of smell, myself.

Then, to crown all, I put my cardigan down the chute with my dirty towels and had to search for a member of staff to retrieve it. Mr B directed me down the twisty stair and said to knock at the door at the foot. What a scary place that was when the door was opened with the heat and steam and noise. Mae in the blue overall was very kind and gave me my cardy. I think she was friendlier to me than anyone else in the club has been, so far.

When I left the club, there was that heavy smell of breweries from the north of the city. People tell me it starts off in the morning like newly-baked bread and then it gets stronger and stronger. I can only smell it by the time it is revolting.

The workmen were still outside and still unloading with a horrible clanging noise and I hurried past them with my head down. I'm not quite sure but I *think* I heard a little whistle as I walked away.

It did seem to have been a particularly unfortunate morning but apart from Jennifer's swimsuit no one else had been affected by my little mistakes and as Mum would say,

"No harm done."

A Visitor to the Club

ALEXANDER WAS A VERY TALL YOUNG MAN who walked with a slightly bowed head which gave him the appearance of wishing to seem not quite so tall. He had long arms and legs and when he was a teenager his mother had lovingly referred to him as "gangly" and at thirty four he was still gangly. He had always worked hard and conscientiously and enjoyed his work and had never interested himself much in athletic pursuits or any of the sybaritic pleasures of the young. His one passion was classical music and opera in particular. Attending the opera is not the best way to meet other young people and Alexander was a lonely young man without quite realising it. Several young ladies had drifted in and out of his life but the stylish girls who attracted him were not the sort who enjoyed the opera and they soon found other escorts to take them to clubs and discos. Consequently Alexander did not have much confidence in his own attractions. But with a thick mop of straight dark hair, very dark blue eyes and a quick wide smile showing large and perfect teeth, Alexander was most certainly not an unattractive man and though his expression often seemed sad, it could change quickly. He would have described himself as "not clever, but a hard worker" but none of his colleagues had ever questioned his cleverness. He had worked hard at school and at University and now worked even harder in an engineering firm. He was design engineer in the Leeds branch of the long-established Scottish firm of Learmonth Engineering.

Alexander's grandfather, David, had come to Leeds to run

this offshoot of the business and he and his family had settled in England.

Alexander had grown up in Leeds and, apart from his years in Cambridge, had always worked there and been content to stay there. After taking his degrees, Alexander had joined the firm and had moved up swiftly and his advancement had nothing to do with his family connections. Though many of his contemporaries now worked in London, Europe and the States, Alexander had been content to stay in Leeds. And yet he did not have a great love for the city.

In spite of his Scottish forbears, his travels had always tended southwards. Any contact with the Glasgow office had been accomplished by letter or telephone and in recent years by fax and e-mail. Now it seemed likely that this visit to Glasgow might result in the offer of a partnership which would necessitate his moving to Scotland.

He knew that his mother Patricia, a statuesque and silent woman, would have liked him to show more interest in Glasgow and the land of her birth. He could not remember her ever putting this into words, but he was aware of it all the same. That knowledge was reinforced when he told her that old Mr Learmonth had summoned him to the Glasgow office for an important meeting the following week. Immediately her face had lit up with joy and for several days she had been uncharacteristically talkative about the trip and when he was to go and why he was to go and how long he would stay and all the other details which she normally ignored when he went away on business. That expression on her face made him feel slightly guilty as, at thirty-four, he had at no time made any effort to visit Scotland nor was Glasgow more than a name to him. There were no relatives left up there now. He often referred to the head office as "North of the border" and that was a quaint phrase when you thought of it. A very alien sort of description. Of course he was familiar with the spectacular views of mountains and rushing rivers which were displayed so lusciously in the calendar which Learmonth Engineering sent out to its clients each year. The country looked wild and beautiful but obviously Glasgow would be different. Much of what one read about Glasgow made it seem a dangerous place with gang warfare, drugs and poverty. But mixed up with this criminal element was a great deal of esoteric culture. One of the funniest comedians that Alexander could think of was Billy Connolly, a Glaswegian. Then there was the Burrell Gallery and the Citizens' Theatre, both known throughout Europe and Glasgow had been the City of Culture in 1990. There was Scottish Ballet though that was not so much his "cup of tea" as his mother would say but Alexander had been bowled over by a performance of *Aida* in Leeds by Scottish Opera. He had thought it wonderful and if it were at all possible, he hoped to attend one or two Scottish Opera productions while he was on this mysterious business trip to Glasgow. Sean Connery was Scottish too and seemed to have been a dashing and romantic film star throughout most of Alexander's life. Alexander had also noticed that in TV plays or in films the statutory Scots accent often belonged to an intellectual, a writer or painter probably. He had mentioned this to his mother once and she had become quite animated as she replied.

"Oh yes, all the books and films always used to have a Scotsman for a doctor anywhere in the world. A doctor educated at Glasgow University or the Anderson School of Medicine was always an excellent doctor. Everyone knew that. And ships' engineers too, they were always Scottish, always Scottish. Trained in the Clyde shipyards, you know. Oh yes they were world famous."

Alexander did not bother to point out that her observations did not quite coincide with his but afterwards he did notice that important medical statements on TV often *were* delivered by consultants with a Scottish accent. Indeed the Surgeon General had a Scottish accent.

Alexander was to fly North on the following Thursday so conjecture was a useless exercise. Gradually as the day of his journey drew near, he felt an increasing interest in the visit.

There was also the intriguing mystery of exactly why Mr Learmonth wanted to see him personally. Would he be offered a partnership? He had considered the possibility, of course, but as he had not been invited North before, it seemed rather sudden.

"Will you go and see the house that I lived in?" asked his mother unexpectedly, when he paid her his usual Wednesday visit. She made few demands on Alexander but this sounded more like a request than a question.

"Would you like me to do that? Certainly, of course I'll do that. You'll have to give me the address."

"It was Doune Gardens and we looked out over trees and down to the River Kelvin. It was a lovely house."

Alexander was surprised to see tears in her eyes. He had never considerd that his mother felt nostalgic for Glagow. She hardly ever mentoned the city or the life she had lived there for the first seven years of her life.

Then she started to laugh.

"I remember when I was a wee girl, just about four, the slugs came into the house. Oh my mother was *horrified.* The hill rose steeply behind the house and I suppose it was damp. There were so many little black slugs all marching in. I thought it was like a party. I quite liked them but she *hated* them. Poor mother. Poor Annie." and Patricia chuckled as she thought about it. Her son was surprised to hear her giggles. Usually she saw the darker side of any given situation. Her amusement was so infectious and so unexpected that Alexander could not help laughing too.

"We spent so much time out the house to avoid them. We went to the pictures and sat through films twice and we went to tearooms. There were some lovely tearooms in Glasgow then, and we stayed much longer at the Arlington than we usually did, talking to everyone, even Mr Sadler. There was a delicious chocolate bar that you could buy at the office in the baths that I loved and I never saw it anywhere else. It had honey and nuts in it, a bit like a Toblerone but just a plain wee bar you know. There was picture of a bee on the wrapper. It was a rare treat to get a piece of it and I suppose it was quite dear but at that time I remember several times I had a whole bar of that to keep me from being hungry and wanting to go home where the slugs were waiting for us" and Patricia went off into gales of laughter again.

Alexander had never seen her laugh so much and though he enjoyed seeing her so happy and he smiled with her, he scarcely understood her humour. He had no mental image of the little girl and her mother of nearly sixty years ago nor did the words "tearoom" or "Arlington" mean much to him.

He just kept smiling and shaking his head at her gently and that seemed to be enough to please her.

Alexander sat opposite James Learmonth, listening dutifully to the quick clipped voice with its narrow vowels and carefully enunciated consonants. It was not at all like the voice of Connolly or 007 or any other of the Scottish accents which he had heard nor was Glasgow like any other city he had visited.

In spite of some clusters of modern buildings, Glasgow was a solid stone-built Victorian city. While the entire centre of Leeds was transformed into a miniature replica of Manhattan, Glasgow had slotted her brick and concrete blocks here and there amongst the massive sandstone as if they were an unfortunate and possibly temporary necessity. The stonework of most of the Victorian buildings had been cleaned and displayed their astonishing detail in the bright Spring sunshine with an arrogant self-confidence.

The interior of James Learmonth's office was also impressive. It was panelled in beautiful dark wood and the upper sashes of the windows were of richly coloured stained glass. Several paintings hung on the wall. Some were of the sea and some were of flamboyant flowers. It was very different from Alexander's utilitarian glass-walled box of an office in Leeds. This room spoke of money and tradition and James himself gave the same impression with his hand-made suit, silk tie and perfectly laundered shirt. His hair was dazzlingly silver-white and his moustache was even more brilliant, or perhaps it only looked brighter against his rosy cheeks. He was just sparklingly clean and expensive looking. He spoke and spoke and Alexander listened dutifully, deciding inwardly that at last he had a perfect example of that word which turns up so often in crosswords "avuncular".

"Well I am so very pleased to see you here Alexander, just delighted. At long, long last you've come up to see us. Come to find your roots, have you? You know we are distantly related? I wouldn't like to put a name to our kinship exactly but your grandmother Annie married my uncle David just a few years before he went to Leeds to open the branch there. But you'll know all about that I expect. Yes, Uncle David and my father, Archie, were very friendly with Annie and her two brothers Johnny and Zander Thomson, that's who you'll be called after I expect. Zander was quite a fellow for the ladies I believe! They all used to play tennis together and there was a lot of dancing. The Plaza was the place for that, even in the afternoons. Of course they were members of the Arlington too. You'll have to pay a visit to the Arlington while you are here my boy, it's the oldest baths club in Britain and perhaps in Europe. We're not quite sure about that. Johnny Thomson was a very fine swimmer, very fine, swam in the Olympics back in twenty something. I was just a kiddy then. They weren't so scientific then of course, couldn't go as fast as they do now . In fact the strokes have all changed now, changed completely I should think. But those young ones in the twenties were quite a *wild* crowd I believe, they had a fine time to themselves. Oh yes, there was Johnny Bruce too, he was secretary of the club for a long time. He lived to a great age just died a few years ago must have been near a hundred the old fellow. He and Bruce Cumming were great pals. Bruce was a great joker, you always got a good laugh with Bruce. His old father had been a member since the year dot. The old codger came in and did his ten lengths every week until he was ninety-six. A grumpy old devil he was too, but amazingly active for his years. I believe he still went daily to the office to see that Bruce and his brother Willie were running the business all right. They must have been pleased to see him! Willie was a strange bloke, a bit of a miser I think. He was friendly with Muirhead Moffat whose father had the big antique shop, excellent business, long established. Willie and Muir, yes they made a good pair, *very careful with the pennies* you know, never spent a sixpence if tuppence would do. Of course they were both very wealthy. They would be wouldn't they. Easy to be wealthy when you don't spend your cash Ha ha ha" and James threw his head back and laughed like a boy. "Funny, a lot of them never married. Like myself of course, you know. Muirhead, Willie Cumming, Johnny B. and Zander. Of course Zandor didn't need to marry. The ladies liked him very much. Even when he seemed like an old man to me they still liked him. But he had a sad end, a sad end, poor soul"

James paused and looked down at the paper clip he was holding. Then he looked up with a wide smile which showed he still had good teeth though they could not compete with his moustache for brightness.

"That's all ancient history now. As I said, I never married myself. Never seemed the right time or never met the right girl, who can say? What about yourself, Alexander? Any special young lady in your life?"

Alexander smiled and shook his head.

"Ah well there's time yet. But if you never marry and you never have children then you feel cut off from the younger generation. You do. I am telling you that you do indeed and that's one reason I'm so pleased to see you up here because I feel you are like one of my own family. I have always felt that, although we have had so little contact over the years. I realise that it is a tenuous thread which connects us, my boy, but really I do feel very close."

His bantering gossipy voice had changed to a more serious tone and he brought out a large snowy handkerchief and blew his nose loudly, then made quite a business of polishing each side of his nose with quick little swipes before replacing the hankie in his pocket.

The long stream of words about the Golden Age of the twenties with those long dead swimmers and tennis players had not prepared Alexander for such a display of emotion. James was only a few years older than Alexander's mother but he seemed like another generation. Perhaps not marrying and not being a parent was the problem, as he had said. Alexander shivered because at thirty-four it seemed very likely that he might not marry either. Would he grow to resemble this garrulous and presumably lonely old man in another thirty-four years? He dragged his attention back to the flow of words which had resumed once more.

"Yes, we are very very pleased with your work Alexander. I have plans for you, great plans. But I will discuss those with you when you have recovered from your journey. Travelling is so tiring, I always think. Now we must see how we will entertain you during your visit. Would you have dinner with me tonight at the Rogano? That's a famous old Glasgow restaurant, very nice cuisine, very quiet and good service, the old style you know. Then tomorrow I expect you would like to visit the Burrell. We are all very proud of our great gallery, though I hear unhappy reports of the roof, leaking you know. Glad it wasn't us that dealt with that one, I can tell you. Then you must pay a visit to the Arlington. You do swim don't you? Oh I knew that any relation of Johnny Thomson would be a swimmer. Compete do you?"

Alexander hurriedly denied that possibility.

"Oh well we'll have a dip and a sauna and a game of billiards then get lunch in the bar, different from the Rogano of course but quite tasty."

Alexander tried to imagine this sophisticated elderly man in swim trunks and failed.

"Anything that you particularly want to do yourself when you are in Glasgow, Alexander?"

"I should very much like to visit the Opera if they are

performing just now, sir."

Alexander had not called anyone "sir" since his school days but somehow this old-fashioned man seemed to merit the appellation.

"The Opera!" it was obviously a stunningly unusual request."That's the Theatre Royal, yes the opera let me see now. Well, I'm rather busy myself tomorrow evening, Saturday too. Is that really what you'd like to do? I'll get in Miss McIver my splendid secretary she likes all that sort of thing, ballet and those high falutin' things, she'll know what to do about it."

A thin severe lady of around fifty appeared immediately and wrote in a small notebook without looking at Alexander, then left the room to fulfil her duty.

"Yes, Miss McIver will see that you get an excellent ticket. She is a devotee of the dance and all that. You can trust Miss McIver absolutely. To return to the baths, the Arlington you know, it is such a long, long association that our families have had with the club. My grandfather William who started the business, was one of the founding members of the Arlington. That was even before old Bob Cumming joined. They were very successful businessmen, chose the best architects and money was no object to begin with although of course the running costs were more than they had bargained for, even with the cheap coal and the low wages... "

He talked on and on and Alexander who had not been at all tired after his short flight from Manchester did start to feel rather drowsy and concentrated on keeping his eyes open as the phrase "long association" repeated itself interminably. He became unclear as to whether it was the association of the two families or the asssociation with the Arlington which was being discussed.

After fifteen minutes Miss McIver returned with a ticket for the dress circle on Friday night. The opera was *Don Giovanni* and Alexander was delighted and thanked her enthusiastically. It was obvious that she was not used to such effusive thanks as she backed towards the door with a meagre and slightly squint smile.

"Never mind her, Alexander she is a terribly shy girl, just let her be. She likes doing wee messages."

"Mr Learmonth, perhaps I might have a walk round Glasgow while it is so bright and sunny. My mother tells me that it's almost as rainy here as in Leeds so perhaps I should take advantage of it while it is dry."

"Of course of course , my boy. What was I thinking of on a lovely day like this. Yes away you go out and have a dauner round the city centre, that just means a wee walk. I hope Patricia has taught you some good old Scottish words. And you can admire some of our beautiful buildings. I don't know what I was doing keeping you inside on such a lovely day. On you go, on you go. I'll call for you tonight at your hotel about seven, on you go now. So good to have you here."

Alexander strode off down the steep hill with its vista of elaborately decorated buildings. He was sorry for the old man and amazed at the enthusiastic welcome he had received. It was all very different from his expectations.

He walked and walked, enjoying the unusual freedom from responsibilities and deadlines. He felt relaxed as he wandered through the busy town centre without once consulting the city map in his briefcase. The weather was bright and cool and his long legs carried him effortlessly up and down innumerable hills with evocative names, West George Street, St Vincent Street, West Nile Street, and then Virginia Street and the Saltmarket. When he reached Clyde Street and the river, he turned westwards again. He loved bridges and the variety across the Clyde delighted him, from the slender suspension bridge and the weighty stone railway bridges to the majestic Kingston bridge with its echoes of a massive Egyptian temple. It was all exciting and yet strangely and inexplicably familiar . He felt that he could enjoy this varied cityscape all day. He had forgotten about eating. No wonder his mother had happy memories of Glasgow. He would ask her much more about it when he got back to Leeds. He remembered her words "sitting in tearooms" and "staying at the baths". Well he was to visit the baths on Saturday with James. He wondered if there were any of the tearooms still existing or if his mother had ever had a meal in the Rogano. At that moment he walked past a strange building with large glass doors like a fire station. It was obviously not that as the gable was decorated in a haywire way with an assortment of square, round and triangular windows. It must be dwelling houses here on the riverfront. Nice location but what an incongruously flippant building in this heavy city of stone. Really some of these post modern architects seemed to have taken leave of their aesthetic senses. Then Alexander forgot the toytown apartment block and caught his breath as a powerful and towering sculpture loomed into view. It was immense and all-encompassing and completely out of scale with its surroundings. Alexander loved its size and strength and perfect design. It was the huge crane which used to load the enormous North British locomotives on to ships sailing to all corners of the world. Though he was familiar with it, no photograph had prepared Alexander for its size and beauty. He suddenly felt light-headed and hailed a taxi.

"Doune Gardens, please," he directed the driver.

After passing more Victorian buildings and driving through a delightful park with a quick glimpse of the University high above the road, quite quickly they turned a sharp corner into a tiny side street which had terrace houses on the right while on the left a dilapidated railing marked the top of a very steep hill which dropped sheer to a noisy but unseen river far below. This hill was covered in trees, virtually a little forest, which were just donning their Spring foliage. The houses must have a delightful view, he realised and he was more understanding of his mother's happy memories. Any child would love to overlook a forest, the starting-off point of so many fairy tales. He asked the driver to wait and he stood beside the railing for a few moments listening to the river below him. This was the river Kelvin and it must have sounded just like this to his mother when she was a little girl of four and the slugs were "marching in" to her kitchen.

He noticed that a railing also ran transversely across the road. The houses on the far side were tenements. There was a gate however and he was relieved to note that strict segregation did not exist between tenement and terrace houses. There were several cars parked in the narrow street and even the taxi did not find it easy to turn. Alexander, who was happiest when driving himself, shuddered at the thought of the taxi backing through the fragile railing and hurtling down the steep hill to the river. He realised that he was tired and hungry and directed the cabby back to his hotel.

That night at the restaurant over fragrant golden soup followed by delicious sole baked, surprisingly, in a paper packet, James gave Alexander more space in the conversation and learned more of the younger man. The two men got on very well indeed.

"And you will visit the Burrell tomorrow? And see Pollok House while you are there, it is very charming. I hope you see the Highland cattle in the park they are splendid animals, there should be some wee calves just now. Then at night you are at the theatre and I hope you enjoy that." his tone suggested that enjoyment of the opera was unlikely. "I'm so glad you have hired a car. We might take a drive out to Loch Lomond on Saturday afternoon. I know a nice little hotel for dinner. Great atmosphere. It's an old drover's inn. You'll like it."

He was certainly taking Alexander under his wing and though the young man found it a slightly suffocating wing, he could not help enjoying the welcome extended by James. It seemed likely that he would be offered a partnership and he found himself enthusiastic about the idea of accepting it in a way that he could never have guessed on the flight to Scotland. It would mean moving to Glasgow and probably his mother would come too. She would like that, he was sure. Then he would perhaps meet a nice Glasgow girl, an afficionado of opera hopefully, marry her and produce the grandchildren which his mother was always hinting were the rightful pleasures of a woman in her sixties. He shook himself free of these fanciful thoughts and returned his attention to the old man. The old man had an unusual and quirky sense of humour after a glass of wine and altogether it was a very enjoyable evening for both of them.

On Friday, after some hours of pleasant browsing in the Burrell and Pollok House, Alexander headed west again in his hired car and drove through the suburbs of Hyndland and Broomhill to Great Western Road which bore exciting directions to "Crianlarich and The North". After driving along this broad boulevard for twenty minutes he followed the sign to Erskine Bridge and found himself on the other side of the Clyde. It was exhilarating. Turning left at Port Glasgow, for no particular reason, he started to climb a very long and steep hill. Towards the top he stopped at a filling station for petrol. Below him the Clyde started to widen out and with its brilliant sparkling water and the vast space above it surrounded by rich blue mountains it was an experience for which no calendar photographs had prepared Alexander. Even in the forecourt, the air was sweet and fresh and he felt he could spread his wings and fly out into that unbounded beauty. It was alarming just how much he was affected by it all.

Higher up the hill he passed housing which looked sad and neglected and further on crowds of noisy teenagers were jostling one another outside a school which though hardly twenty years old looked ready for demolition. Obviously life was no nearer perfection here than in Leeds, but what great compensations there were.

On Saturday morning with the exquisite music of the previous evening still flooding his brain, Alexander found the Arlington Baths club without difficulty. James had directed him to turn left "at that diabolical booze shop with the grotesque paintings on the windows, shouldn't be allowed" which led into a short street with a mixture of elderly tenements, harsh new brick apartments and the shabby but elegant Arlington with its classical frontage. Alexander smiled as he realised that the cul-de-sac was a microcosm of the city itself.

A smart little blonde woman in a blue overall greeted him and directed him to the office but no one was there and Alexander peered through a door at the swimming pool which lay beyond, empty and blue. He did not find it at all inviting and he wondered why he had not been able to say "no" to James. Swimming was possibly the last occupation on earth that he would choose for a Saturday morning. Would he have the same difficulty in some business situation? That would be bad. Very bad news indeed. James was so overpoweringly *nice* but presumably he had a harder side to him or he could not have run the company so successfully for so long. When would Alexander come up against that steelier side of James he wondered.

Suspended on ropes above the pool for its entire length were eight metal rings, presumably for swinging from one end of the pool to the other. "Hmm, Tarzan lives again," thought Alexander, that was something which he did not mean to attempt. Also there were two trapezes with platforms for boarding. Did one board a trapeze? How very energetic it all was! Not to say atavistic. Surely James would never indulge in that sort of athleticism… not nowadays anyway but it was very old equipment, just as old as James. Perhaps even his own grandmother Annie had swung over that blue water in her heavyweight swimsuit. His mother had described the regulation woollen suit to him once. It was large and solid and red with white binding and a large white A for Arlington on the tummy. Patricia had always believed that the A stood for Annie as her mother had two friends also called Annie and the child had been assured that only ladies called Annie were allowed to wear the letter. He thought of his mother chuckling at his Grandmother's oft-repeated joke.

"When there are three Annies together, one of them is bound to be daft."

He remembered another story of his mother's about the little girl who always swam away fast from Patricia.

"I just wanted to play with her but she was a timid wee

thing and I was always such a big lump of a creature."

As he thought of his mother as a child and those long gone young women teaching their toddlers to swim he felt more enthusiastic about plunging in to this strangely quiet pool.

"Can I help you, sir?" said a pleasant but authoritative voice. It was the bathsmaster Jim Brannan. Explaining that he was a guest of James Learmonth softened Jim's manner and he directed Alexander to the changing rooms and the showers. It was years since he had swum so he might as well get in a bit of practice before James arrived.

Though the place was certainly not luxurious, it was clean and practical and because of the associations which were surfacing in his mind it was becoming more and more fascinating. The showers were magnificent and made him think that he might never enjoy the stingy trickle of a modern shower again. As each corner brought to mind another little anecdote of his mother's he realised how wrong he had been to think that she did not speak much of Glasgow. He must search out the gymnasium and the parallel bars that she had mentioned.

After the hot shower the water felt very cold but after swimming to the deep end and back, he no longer felt the chill. His only stroke was the breast stroke which he swam with his head held high out of the water and his chin leading the way. It was not an elegant style but because he had such long legs and arms, he moved quickly through the water.

The blonde lady in blue appeared carrying a tall pile of clean folded towels.Then he saw another blonde girl in blue with a mass of used towels which she proceeded to drop down a chute arrangement in an alcove. She then disappeared through a door and could be seen descending to some lower regions. The first girl walked past with a scarlet vacuum cleaner. The bathsmaster strode puposefully to the showers with a mop and pail and energetic scrubbing was heard. One of the blue overalls again appeared with a heavy bucket of water and a large bottle of cleaning detergent. A burly older man with a large face and bald head very carefully checked the temperature of the pool then walked to the deep end and obviously switched something off as the strong vibration which Alexander had noticed in the water ceased immediately. It was much pleasanter without the vibration. Then this same man lifted down a coiled black hosepipe from its storage space on the wall and carried it ponderously to the other side of the pool. It must have been fearfully heavy and the man walked slowly and carefully. Outside the shower room, he threw it to the ground and started to uncoil it for use. As he struggled with the heavy wayward rubber pipe, Alexander remembered a favourite illustration of his childhood showing Laocoon fighting with the Serpent. Like his mythical predecessor the old man eventually triumphed over the hosepipe.

Just as Alexander was telling himself that he should leave the water and try the rings or the trapeze while no one else was in the pool, another swimmer appeared. She was a slim compact woman though she no longer had the fragility of a girl. She might have been anything between late thirties or late forties. She nodded to Alexander in a friendly way, then diving in at the deep end, she swam a breadth of the pool underwater. Then she started to swim lengths with a strong puposeful crawl. After ten lengths, she started to vary her stroke, always moving through the water smoothly and speedily. It was very impressive and Alexander realised his own inadequacies more fully as he watched her. Then he thought he must be staring in a rude way. It would have been nice to speak to her but as each length was completed by an impressive tumbleturn which took her many yards into the next length, there was no chance of striking up a conversation. He began to dread James seeing his futile attempts at swimming. He could never match up to his brilliant great-uncle Johnny, the swimming champion. Perhaps James would decide that such a poor swimmer could never be a partner in his distinguished firm. These old Scotsmen could be very eccentric, his mother always said.

Another ten minutes passed and still no sign of James.

Suddenly a very pretty girl arrived and in moments was emerging from the shower room. She was curvaceous and had a mane of reddish brown curly hair, which she was trying in vain to cram into a bathing cap. She twisted it up then shook it loose. She bent over from the waist and tried to plait it as it hung down, then changed her mind. She flung it back over her shoulders again and sighed. Eventually she did manage to stuff most of it into the rubber swimcap. The tendrils which were still visible were most fetching. She really had a wonderful figure, her swimsuit was no larger than it needed to be and her performance had been magnificent. Alexander was fascinated. As she walked gingerly down the steps and into the water she flashed a smile at Alexander and set off with a stroke which was as ungainly as his own. Somehow he was delighted that she was a poor swimmer.

As he swam once more towards the deep end, he noticed that the older woman had stopped and was treading water. She had an expression of great sadness on her face and when she saw Alexander so close to her, she dipped her face in the water. He believed that it was to hide tears but could not be sure. When she surfaced again she smiled a small hurried smile to him and pushed herself into another powerful length. Was she trying to escape some part of her life? perhaps swimming was as good a way as any. She was a very interesting woman although of course the younger glamorous one was gorgeous.

At the shallow end the pretty girl started to chat to Alexander. Her speech was punctuated with little charming gasps. She explained that she was a new member and always tried to swim fifteen lengths no matter how breathless it made her.

"Have you been a member long? I haven't seen you on a Saturday before. It's a lovely old-fashioned place, isn't it? I don't know anywhere quite like it and its got such great gym equipment. Do you work out often? I always try to do twenty minutes every Saturday."

Alexander could not find the energy to explain the

complicated reasons for his visit to the baths, so mumbled that he was a new member. He wondered if she would come for a drink with him if he asked her but decided against it as his time was so ruled by James Learmonth at this moment.

Just then Jim Brannan walked around the pool towards them and, kneeling down, delivered the telephone message that "Mr Learmonth has a chill this morning and will not be swimming and would Alexander please meet him at the Rogano at midday."

It was almost a relief to leave the red-haired girl and her breathless chatter in the pool. Perhaps in the future, when he was a partner in Learmonth Engineering, he might join the Arlington and see her again and he might take her for a drink.

Or perhaps he would improve his swimming and speak to the interesting woman with the secret sorrow.

Winking at the Brim

THE WATER APPEARED TO BOIL as great bubbles of air gushed to the surface. Lilias was crouched at the shallow end of the swimming pool. She had to crouch to stay beneath the surface for warmth. She was so tall now that the water did not even reach her waist, where at one time she could not stand with her mouth above the surface.

Sometimes that seemed long ago and sometimes it seemed quite recently.

The stream of bubbles did not come consistently and some were larger than others and sometimes they stopped altogether for a few seconds though there was usually a great rush of them after a pause like that. She had been told that the air was forced into the swimming pool to create a little disturbance on the surface of the water, in order to send the tiny particles of dust which gathered there when the pool lay still and unused, towards the deep end, where the filter would remove them from the water. Perhaps other detritus was also swept towards its annihilation at the deep end, stuff like hairs and drowned beetles and pieces of Elastoplast. Lilias ignored those gross possibilities and concentrated on the dust motes as she could visualise her cat's water-bowl each morning, dim and uninviting. She enjoyed washing the bowl and offering a sparkling fresh drink to Sidney. He deserved it.

Like most girls of her age, Lilias was an unpredictable mixture of the practical and the romantic. She was pleased to know exactly why the bubbles were there, but she would have liked a more exciting explanation.

When she and her mother had holidayed in Greece last Easter they had taken the hair-raising bus journey to Delphi and stayed there for two nights in a little hotel which clung to the mountainside by the skin of its teeth. Those days had been the best part of the holiday for Lilias. By rising early, she and her mother had been able to explore the entire site before the bus-loads of tourists arrived to desecrate the amazing and inspiring antiquity of the place. In her mind's eye, Lilias peopled the ruined remains of the temple, the theatre and the high sports arena with beautiful and stately Greeks. All were tall and athletically built, had perfect classical features and were dressed in flowing colourful robes. They wore wreaths on their noble brows or carried large bouquets of flowers and all bore a distinct resemblance to the folk in the paintings of Alma Tadema, that imaginative Victorian painter of classical scenes. Lilias adored it all and lost herself in thought until she would hear the tooting of the buses far beneath her, heralding the arrival of the multinational mobs. When she heard that ominous sound she would climb up the steep mountain to the sports ground, which was at the very top, and run several circuits around the track. It would be ages before anyone reached that part of the site, some of them never did reach it.

As she ran in the fresh thin air, with her red shorts and T-shirt transformed in her mind to an orange chiton, she could almost see the three judges who waited to award her the laurel wreath. Afterwards, as Lilias was lightly jumping down the mountain, all the poor tourists would be toiling upwards, sweat on their brows and cameras at the ready. Of course the cameras were an excellent excuse for a short rest on that punishing slope.

Then there was the place of the Oracle, the holy of holies, the raison d'etre of this entire complex, built so high and so far from anywhere. It must have been a long and hazardous journey from Athens before the tourist coach was invented, but it must have been worth it to see the Oracle. The Delphic Oracle. One guide book said that Delphi meant dolphin but that seemed highly unlikely so far above the sea.

Her mother said that those ancients must have had a rare old time to themselves when they came there, what with the theatre and the sports-ground and lots of shops no doubt, just like a holiday camp… something like an antique Butlin's. But her mother had no romance in her.

Lilias was struck by the down to earth practicality of the implements required by the high priestess to make her prophecies. There was a tripod with other smaller items which Lilias had now forgotten, but they all fitted together when not in use, just like a desk tidy. For some reason, the tripod had been placed over the hole in the ground from which the supernatural fumes issued. Then Pythia, the high priestess, who would be tall and sinuous as Pythia meant python, breathed in or inspired these fumes and she was able to predict the future. That must be where the word inspiration came from. It was a great story and Lilias loved it and read it over several times in the guide book each night. It even gave several examples of the prophecies, omitting to mention whether they had come to pass or not. Of course they might have lost something in translation, but to Lilias they sounded suspiciously like the vague all-embracing generalities to be found in common or garden horoscopes. However no doubt they would be more impressive delivered in Greek verse, by a willowy priestess, there amongst the clouds on the mountainside. It might be good idea to study Greek at school next year instead of German, she thought.

It was during that night that Lilias first thought of the bubbles at the Arlington baths and how similar they seemed to this spiritual gas of Delphi, rising to the surface so mysteriously. She decided that when she returned home, she would experiment with breathing in those bubbles at the baths. Even as a child those bubbles had intrigued her. She enjoyed the sensation of holding her hand amongst them and the continous bumping of the soft round ephemeral objects seemed satisfying, familiar and evocative. Eventually, she decided that it reminded her of holding her mother's breast in her cupped hand when she suckled as an infant.

She watched her mother swimming up and down. She was using the back crawl now. Really it was bizarre for a woman of her age to enjoy swimming so much and to swim so many lengths.

Any moment now she would stop at the shallow end and look over at her daughter quizzically, eyebrows lifted, head tilted and ask

"Going to have a swim today, darling? Water's gorgeous!"

She wouldn't say more. She would want to, but she wouldn't. Then she would dip below the water and push off hard from the side with her strong little legs and shoot towards the deep end again, leaving Lilias scowling and immobile.

It was not that her mother was a better swimmer or anything, though she was better at lots of other things of course, cooking and sewing and shopping and driving. Earning money, too. But Lilias had been able to beat her mother at the crawl for nearly two years now. It was just that her mother enjoyed the water so much and wanted everyone else to enjoy it too. And she was a pretty fair swimmer for her age.

It seemed such a long time since Lilias had really had fun in the water, years and years really. She did love it when she was little, she remembered that.

She huddled down beside the bubbles and felt the gentle turbulence in the water. She had stopped trying to find a magical inspiration from the bubbles. At first, when she had returned from the Greek holiday, she had sniffed strenuously at the chlorine-laden air above the bubbles on several occasions until one day she saw an elderly lady looking at her very strangely and she never did it again.

The next thing would be Jim Brannan rushing out of his office and expecting her to swim two hundred lengths of the crawl or practice her tumbleturns or something. He was always so jokey and cheerful with his demands. She couldn't stand it.

Her mother seemed to like him fine, always having a few

quick laughing words with him each time she saw him. Come to think of it her mother was always talking to men, old ones and young ones. It was strange how friendly she acted towards them considering the poor opinion she had of men in general. That was understandable when you thought of how Dad had behaved, disappearing like that across the Atlantic and existing now only as a voice on the telephone. A voice that always assured his daughter how very much he loved her. But what did that mean? What was love over the telephone? You could not go swimming with a voice. And even the telephone voice was more real than the grey-haired stranger who visited her every other year with the two little boys who also called him Dad.

Then her mother had been really let down by her lawyer. Lilias remembered how distressed and angry her mother used to be sometimes, making phone calls and writing letters. Though she had tried to hide it from her little nine-year old, Lilias had noticed and worried. Then there was the accountant and the bank manager who had both made such a mess of her mother's income tax. And now, with the attic-conversion, her mother once more was struggling with an officious planner and a dilatory architect. Honestly, being an adult was a series of stressful situations and it was difficult to understand why her friends were so desperate to grow up. Lilias was tallest of all her friends and knew she looked the most grown-up and was envied a little because of that.

There now, her mother had stopped half-way up the pool and yes, she was talking to a man. Her arms were stretched straight as she held the metal bar which ran around the pool just above the surface of the water, and her head was tipped back to look at the tall old man who stood above her on the edge of the pool. She was nodding and smiling and the man looked pleased. He wore blue jogging trousers and a red sweat shirt and looked very smart and was obviously going to the gym for a work-out. His erect lithe figure showed that he was a regular attender at the club.

"Ridiculous," thought Lilias "you'd think a man of that age

would have something better to do with his time. And Mother, too, you'd think she was enjoying talking to him."

Of course her mother talked to women too. Her mother talked to everyone. And she still managed to swim fifty or sixty lengths, at least she said she did. Lilias had never checked up on that, but her mother was very truthful.

Too truthful sometimes.

Lilias turned around and let the bubbles ripple up her back like a sort of massage.

Now her mother was beside her at the shallow end again and Lilias tried not to catch her eye. She knew how pathetically pleased her mother would be if she started to swim. Her mother was having the little rest that she took "to renew the oxygen in my muscles before I sprint", then she would crawl two lengths. She wasn't really very fast, but faster than some. Faster than most women of her age. But not *really* fast. Slow compared to her own crawl, when she felt like it. Which wasn't to-day.

Here was that man with the beard. Just watch, her mother would speak to him. Yes, there they were, he was grinning and walking through the water towards her mother as he untangled his goggles. He was quite handsome, in a mature sort of way because he must be nearly forty. People must be so keen to come swimming when they were that age. Of course her mother was years older than him even, at least five or six years.

She noticed that her mother stayed well below the surface of the water as she talked to the bearded man. That would be to hide her plumpness, Lilias supposed. Though what did it matter at her age? Older women were supposed to be plump. She and her mother were so different now that she had grown so much this last year. She had always been paler than her mother and now she was tall and thin and pale, where her mum was short and fat and rosy. Perhaps fat was cruel.

No, she was fat.

Lilias moved out of the bubbles. They were becoming ticklish and unpleasant and she felt depressed and useless.

She thought of last Christmas when she had helped herself to rather a lot of red wine. How queasy she had felt next morning, really awful. Her mother had suggested an Alka Seltzer and that had helped. With that memory clear in her mind, she felt much better and even smiled to herself.

She lay back amongst the bubbles again and assumed the shape of the two large white indigestion tablets, fizzing and dissolving in the glass of water.

How marvellous to dissolve and fade away and never have to worry about adult problems.

Then he arrives. The new member. His name is Donald, I've found out that much. He's much older than me of course, seventeen at least and he's so gorgeous. He's so tall. And such eyes! Lustrous eyes. Skinny? What's wrong with skinny, makes a change from everyone else in sight. Just watch, he'll smile to mother!

He does! I can't believe it! I don't suppose he even sees me. Well he wouldn't, when I have dissolved, would he.

My goodness he has changed his clothes really fast and he hasn't spent long in the shower either. Must be keen to get in the water. No, he's going to try and swing on the rings again. Oh Donald, don't do that. Not after last week. Please. But I suppose it really is hard when you are long and lanky and you haven't used them as long as you can remember. Oh shame, he's in the water again. He is so strong at pulling himself up on to the side, terribly strong. He's having lots of practice at that, anyway. Oh, what a shame, don't do it any more Donald.

There's Mother giving him advice now. Predictable. Funny to think she can't go on them herself but doles out advice. I've never seen her on the rings anyway. Maybe long ago when she wasn't so fat. I suppose she taught me long ago. I expect he'll improve with practice.

Why doesn't he just swim? He could do a reasonable breast-stroke, if he put his head a bit lower in the water. Chlorine might hurt his lustrous eyes, though.

He's going to try the trapeze now and I just cannot watch.

Lilias moved out of the bubbles and sat on the step.

At either side of the curved corner of the pool was a set of three steps descending into the water where they met on a common landing or platform which was only about three inches higher than the bottom of the pool. Those three inches were of vital importance to a young child, for even at the shallow end, a three-year old would have difficulty standing on the bottom and keeping its face above water. That little landing gave enough height for a two-year old to take those first adventurous steps through, what was to it, deep water without a helping hand. Though the distance was scarcely a yard, Lilias could remember clearly how far it seemed to be from the lowest step of one flight to the lowest step of the other, and the feelings of terror and pleasure and relief when she had reached her goal. Then she had progressed to shooting off from one step to the other without touching the platform. That was the beginning of swimming. Her Mother had never believed in arm-bands or swim-rings and Lilias had not had quite the same freedom as other safely-buoyed children had, to propel themselves all over the place. However, she had learned the realities of what you had to do to keep afloat, much sooner than those others and by the time she was three was a confident and accomplished swimmer. Though she always had that sense of relief when her feet touched the platform again.

Later, of course, she played at the deep end where the steps were the same, except that the drop from the platform to the bottom of the pool was many feet instead of a few inches.

Her mother touched Lilias on the arm.

"Dreaming, darling? I think I'll go out now and wash my hair. No hurry, to-day. Take your time."

Lilias looked at her mother with a slight nod of the head and no expression of any kind.

Was her mother being ironic when she said there was no hurry? Lilias would have been happy not to have come there in the first place. Mothers were so hard to understand.

With a last look at the bubbles, she slowly left the water. Donald had gone long ago so no chance of speaking to him. How could she anyway? What did you say to a man when you were thirteen. Even if he were a member of the same club.

He was awfully handsome, but what a rotten swimmer. As he had thrown his towel into the wire basket from a rather unnecessary distance and disappeared through the swing doors she felt that she should feel forlorn. She liked that word very much. It was a word that resonated, as the visiting American teacher would say.

Forlorn and resonated, she liked both of those words.

Lilias dried her hands on the towel which she had left on the bench and leaped for a ring. With absolute control of her long legs and apparently no effort, she travelled gracefully on the rings to the deep end and back again. As she dropped lightly off the last ring, she saw that her mother had not yet entered the showers, but was standing, looking over her shoulder. She was watching her daughter's prowess and looked pleased and relaxed.

Lilias felt really happy for the first time that day and, diving into the water, swam a swift twenty lengths of a smooth un-splashing crawl with a copybook tumbleturn at the end of every length.

The Family Pool

The family pool is hardly ever still.
Across its surface is a constant chill caress
Of angers, joys, surprises,
While below surge hot currents,
Sweeping us round in helpless unknowing conflict.
Interactions in the water create good and bad
But seldom stillness,
Never calm.

Streams and rivers overflow our pool
Bringing mud and silt,
And sometimes joyous waterfalls or whirlpools.
Some days the rain of faraway events makes its effect,
Monotonous
Diluting
But adding welcome depths.

On occasion,
Though a strong swimmer,
Exhausted by the changing temperatures and ceaseless motion,
I leave the water
And sit alone amongst the reeds.

Starlight at the Arlington

THE TAXI TURNED SLOWLY into the narrow side street and gingerly made its way over the pot-holed road and past the dilapidated pavements which only a recent earthquake might explain. On each side, the tenements, though not derelict, were dirty and un-maintained with mouldering cardboard behind broken windows, cracked and sagging front steps and a lack of verticality in the gap-toothed palings. One block of flats was supported by an immense structure of scaffolding which covered the entire facade and extended to the middle of the road. Presumably, without this crutch, the eight apartments of this building would have crumbled helplessly into a pile of red sandstone dust. A few very old cars were parked, some of them unlikely to leave the street of their own volition. It was November and four or five leaves still clung to a dusty little tree which grew beside a basement window in one of the areas.

As the driver negotiated his way around the scaffolding, he avoided a very thin cat, apparently bent on suicide.

The occupant of the taxi gazed with interest at this scene of poverty and despair. It was very different from anything which he had so far encountered in Glasgow, very different. He had seen the glorious opulence of the City Chambers, the dignified splendour of the University's Bute Hall, the dramatic richness of the Theatre Royal, the large hospitable flats of the West End with their soaring ceilings, and the various wealthy homes of the South side. They had not been at all what he had expected to find in Glasgow. Some of the large classical buildings had reminded him slightly of his own beautiful city, very slightly.

But this sad litter-strewn, mean little street, yes this was what he had been led to expect of the once-great industrial city. Could this be the right place? Was it likely that a prestigious masseur would practise his art in this slum? The cab stopped at the brick wall with which the street ended abruptly.

"That'll be ten bob, mister."

The driver looked sharply over his shoulder at the strange young man in the shabby fur coat who seemed to glare through the window at the grimy columns of the entrance to the Arlington Baths. It was a typical dark but mild November day, with intermittent rain and the ankle-length musquash coat must have been cumbersome and much too warm. The young man did not move and the taxi driver had a good look at him. With his deep-set eyes glittering under long bushy eyebrows and his unusually thick red lips, his face was an unusual one. Though his sharp cheekbones and hollow cheeks spoke of a thinness bordering on emaciation, the collarless neck which arose from the coat was that of a prize-fighter.

"He's got the muscles o' a bloody bull." thought the driver to himself. "Wouldnae like tae grapple wi' that yin!"

He repeated his request for the fare.

The eyes turned sharply then the head turned slowly towards the driver,

"Pleass?"

"Ten shullins, surr. Ten shillings, unnerstaund?"

The driver held up two hands with ten blunt fingers extended, smiling and nodding his head encouragingly.

"Yer owin' me ten shullins, surr. The ferr is TEN SHULLINS."

By this time the cabbie was talking very slowly and very loudly.

At last the man understood and produced a large wallet, dangerously like a hand-bag to the cabbie's eyes.

"Pleass. Take zis. Enoff? Yis?"

His voice was deep but had a little break in it at times, like a teenager's. The vowels were smothered as though he had swallowed them, but the delivery of the words was sharp, like his cheek bones.

"Aye, plenty, plenty thanks. Ah'll gie ye yer chinge. Right, that's ten bob makes two and. therr's three, fower and wan makes five. That's fine noo."

The passenger took the notes with an air of incomprehension.

It was obvious to the driver that he would be unlikely to get a tip, just lucky to get the right fare, he supposed.

The young man still sat without moving, looking now at the buildings on the right. Unlike the rest of the street, this was a short row of two-storey houses, no doubt respectable and desirable at one time, but now occupied by squatters and even more disreputable than the tenements. In a few months they would disappear when demolition orders were put into effect.

Generally, when their destination was reached, passengers would start to fidget, gathering coat, umbrella, newspaper, briefcase or shopping bags. They would sit on the edge of the seat and fumble for the door handle. But this fellow sat still. His stillness was unnatural.

Then, very smoothly, he turned his head again to the left and regarded the Arlington Club.

"Ah'll tell ye, it's better inside than ootside, mister. Jist as weel, eh?"

The cabbie grinned but the man made no response except to jut his chin more forward. The prominent masseter muscle on his jaw pulsed gently as he sat motionless with the five notes clutched in one hand and the wallet in the other.

As the car radio spluttered out requests for his services in other parts of the city, the driver coughed and moved in his seat, unsure how to get rid of this peculiar passenger. Then, turning only his eyes, the thin young man very slightly tossed his head, much as a nervous horse does.

The driver understood and was out of the cab and holding open the passenger door in double quick time.

With deliberation and showing a pair of beautiful brown leather boots, the man in the fur coat emerged from the taxi.

He moved extremely slowly. It was the slowness of complete, muscular control, full of grace and power. It was the slowness of a python descending from a high rock on a hot day.

Still gazing at the shabby dripping frontage of the old baths club, he murmured something whch sounded like "Cross the Piano" to the driver and put the ten-shilling note into the breast pocket of the driver's jacket.

"That's a funny bugger, right enuff." thought the driver.

After ascending the five steps, Rudolf Nureyev rang the bell of the Arlington Baths.

"Aye, whit can I do for ye, surr?"

The grizzled man was not welcoming, as he held the door less than half open and peered in disbelief at the fur coat.

"I 'ave come for massage. I 'ave appointment vis Carleel."

"Oh, it's Jimmy Carlisle ye're wantin, but Ah'm afraid that's no' possible. Ye see this is a private club an' ye're no' a member an' Ah canny let ye in. Ah'm sorry, surr."

And without sounding at all sorry, he shut the door.

Joe Cox was acting bathsmaster, a role for whch he was perhaps not best fitted. Joe was nearing sixty at this time and apart from five years of active service in the war, he had been a member of the staff at the Arlington baths since he had left school at fourteen and for Joe, the rules of the Arlington were engraved on tablets of stone. His first job had been designated 'pants-boy' and his main task had been to collect the voluminous blue pants that male swimmers wore, rinse and dry them and return each pair to the correctly numbered hook in the office ready for the next time that they might be required. In the shower room was a wire basket where the well trained member would deposit his wet pants after a swim. Unfortunately many members, spoiled by adoring mothers and wives, dropped their sopping gear beside the pool, on the floor of changing rooms, behind benches in the Turkish or steam rooms, just anywhere it suited them in fact and poor young Joe was forced each day to hunt over the entire premises for mislaid drawers. If the pants were not hanging on the correct hook the next time a member required them, there was hell to pay. Mr Sadler the bathsmaster was a stern and unbending man and he had the power to sack Joe on the spot, at a time when jobs were hard to find. It was a nightmare for the boy and throughout his life, in times of stress, Joe would still dream of searching through a vast building for elusive blue garments.

Nowadays Joe was almost as unhappy as bathsmaster as he had been as pants-boy. Hard-working, honest and reliable, he was an excellent lieutenant, but he had not the authority, tact, style or even the desire to be a general.

Now, who was this funny looking geyser in the fur coat and what should he do about him? Through the glass panel of the door, he could see the man still standing there. If Joe did not have authority himself he recognised it in others and this guy in the fur coat exuded authority and confidence, though he looked like a tramp. He seemed to have no intention of leaving the doorway.

A passing member listened to Joe's dilemma and advised him to "invite the bloke in while you check up with Carlisle."

When Joe opened the door, Nureyev was standing with his back to him, contemplating a thin brown dog which sat on the stairs of the opposite house, alternately biting its hind-quarters and gazing anxiously up the street.

"Will ye come in now, surr, and we'll see what we can do. Jist wait here, now."

The young man glided into the outer hall and stood on the exact spot indicated by the peremptory and unsmiling older man, only raising his eyebrows slightly when Joe shouted over his shoulder as he walked away, "Ye'll hiv tae take yer boots aff if you come ony further, yer no' allowed tae wear them inside."

Nureyev found the words unintelligible but recognised them as an order.

"There' a right funny yin oot here, Jimmy. He's wantin' a massage."

"Is thur?" grunted the small man with the bowed back without looking up.

He was dressed in a white shirt, made transparent by the energy of his occupation and the steaminess of the room. Through the shirt his sleeveless singlet and his deformity were clearly visible. On his meagre and slightly bowed legs were grey flannel trousers purchased from the boy's department of D. M. Hoey, the long-established Glasgow outfitters. He grunted and sweated as he worked in the small steamy room. In front of him, face down on a marble slab, lay a mountainous naked figure. Jimmy Carlisle worked on the broad back as a good baker works on bread. His long strong thumbs pushed the flesh into little mounds with such force that gasps were forced from the man on the slab. It was difficult to judge whether they were gasps of pain or pleasure which came from the small mouth underneath the black moustache,

"Aye he's a right funny bugger in a fur coat. Says he's goat an appointment, an' he didnae seem tae ken this wis a privit club."

Jimmy Carlisle, renowned masseur, international bicycling champion and world traveller continued his pinching, pushing, slapping and beating without replying. No one would have guessed that the hunch-backed figure had once been a fine athlete, but crouching over his handlebars for thousands of miles, coupled with his profession and the passing years had contributed to his present shape. Crowds had once lined the roads to cheer him as he sped through Europe and right into Soviet Russia. It was a mystery how in those days of the Cold War, passports and visas were made available and the Iron Curtain was drawn aside for Jimmy Carlisle. Perhaps his athletic skill was sufficient to make him welcome. He also exercised his professional skills throughout the USSR, where the ancient art of massage was perhaps more appreciated that in his own country. It was also rumoured that Jimmy's father had had close ties with Russia in those turbulent days, when fear of the Red Clyde struck terror into the hearts of the British Establishment.

Whatever the reason, Jimmy Carlisle was not only

welcomed in Russia, he was feted as a hero. He travelled extensively and was known as a sportsman and as a fine masseur.

"Oh aye, Ah remember noo, Scottish Ballet phoned me up. Some big bug hud pu'ed a muscle in his airm whin he wis liftin' yin o' thae bally reenies. An' Ah said Ah wid fix it fur'm. Bring him in, Joe."

This was a long speech for Jimmy and it was delivered in short grunting phrases as he continued his energetic work on the man with the moustache.

After removing the boots and bright green socks from the strongest and most elegant feet in the world, Nureyev followed Joe Cox along the hall, around a corner, through two swing doors, and into the yellow-tiled massage room. He gazed with an undisguised astonishment at the large man with the moustache as he lay on the marble slab, a creature so different to himself that he might have belonged to another species.

Jimmy scarcely looked up from his task, but mumbled,

"Ah'm busy the now, jist wait therr a minit."

Nureyev stood immobile with his cold, still glance following every movement of the masseur.

"Who did ye say ye wur? Whit's yer name?"

" I am NUREYEV!" and it was magnificently said, in the voice of one who knows he is a star.

But he was not the only star in that room.

"Aye, weel, ye kin tak that manky coat aff and sit doon till Ah'm ready."

The dancer allowed the coat to drop to the floor where he stood and with no further regard for it, seated himself on a bench and folding his arms, gazed at the border of decorative tiles on the wall.

"Here, Joe, take that auld coat outae here, It shouldnae hiv been in here in the furst place. Ah think it's jumpin'."

After a slight hesitation, Joe picked up the coat and held it with distasteful fingers for a few moments before he bundled it awkwardly under his arm and left the room.

The strange thing was, that Nureyev appeared much larger without the coat than when wearing it. Now in his thirties, his muscles were starting that climb towards heaviness which all male dancers dread and none can avoid. The long hours of rehearsal and performance had laid down layer upon layer of muscle and the slender litheness of his youth was slowly disappearing. The short-sleeved blue T-shirt revealed the muscled shoulders and arms required to carry eight stone of ballerina above his head around a large stage, for even the most delicate of those fairy creatures is a bundle of tightly packed and heavy muscles, and they must be carrried with grace and tenderness and never, never dropped. Through his well worn jeans showed the legs which had the power to send that over-developed upper body soaring higher than any other dancer since Nijinsky.

The fat man with the moustache had finally reached the end of his pummelling and, with a few slaps and groans, he was helped to his feet and he draped himself in a white sheet. He was much improved by the drapery and he walked across the small hot room with a surprising degree of dignity. As he reached the door, he turned and looked back curiously at the man on the bench.

"Hello… I say, I think I know who you… I think my wife said you were in Glasgow and she's going to your show tonight … in the Royal, isn't it? I hope you enjoy your massage… it's a terrific experience… though I'll tell you, I'm exhausted now, just exhausted… but Jimmy's just great you know. Well good bye then. Terribly exciting to meet you… can't wait to tell my wife. 'Bye."

But with a small, polite nod to the fat man, Nureyev had started to discard his clothes and almost immediately was standing naked in his unique muscular beauty.

"It ees 'ere, ze pine." he indicated the triceps of his left arm, "Las' night, ven I leefting Olga, zees mossel goes 'cleek cleek' an' all sroo ze night is ver' zore, ver' ver' zore. I not sleep, I am crying."

The statement was simple and innocent but Jimmy, used to

the dead pan delivery of Glasgow humour, found it hard to judge if a joke were intended.

"Aye. Right then."

"Now, I lie don 'ere, yes?".

A fresh towel was spread and the great dancer lay down on the slab, conscious that no such body had ever lain there before.

"Aye," said Jimmy, "Right, noo then." and he set to work with his angry face and his deformed back and his magic hands.

"Aye, ye've goat a guid body therr, Mister. Aye it's very strong, weel muscled. A wee bit over-developed in places but niver mind that, though. An' is that the sair bit? Jist therr? Ah'll soon fix that fur ye. Ah'll see ye through. Ah'll soon hiv it as righ' as rain. Ye'll be liftin' that lassie the night, nae boather at a'."

Jimmy was a star himself and he knew how to treat an equal.